Emma

商務印書館

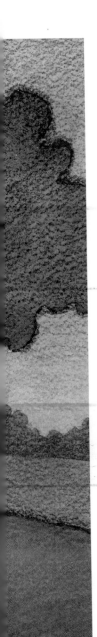

Name of Book: Emma
Author: Jane Austen
Text adaptation and notes: Derek Sellen
Activities: Derek Sellen, Kenneth Brodey
Editors: Rebecca Raynes, Victoria Bradshaw
Design and art direction: Nadia Maestri
Computer graphics: Simona Corniola
Illustrations: Alfredo Belli
Edition: ©2003 Black Cat Publishing
                  an imprint of Cideb Editrice, Genoa, Canterbury

系 列 名：Black Cat 優質英語階梯閱讀 · Level 6
書　　名：愛　瑪
責任編輯：傅　伊
封面設計：張　毅
出　　版：商務印書館 (香港) 有限公司
　　　　　香港筲箕灣耀興道3號東滙廣場8樓
　　　　　http://www.commercialpress.com.hk
印　　刷：中華商務彩色印刷有限公司
　　　　　香港新界大埔汀麗路36號中華商務印刷大廈
版　　次：2004年2月第1版第1次印刷
　　　　　© 2004 商務印書館 (香港) 有限公司
　　　　　ISBN 962 07 1696 5
　　　　　Printed in Hong Kong

出版説明

　　本館一向倡導優質閱讀，近年來連續推出了以 "Q" 為標識的 "Quality English Learning 優質英語學習" 系列，其中《讀名著學英語》叢書，更是香港書展入選好書，讀者反響令人鼓舞。推動社會閱讀風氣，推動英語經典閱讀，藉閱讀拓廣世界視野，提高英語水平，已經成為一種潮流。

　　然良好閱讀習慣的養成非一日之功，大多數初、中級程度的讀者，常視直接閱讀厚重的原著為畏途。如何給年輕的讀者提供切實的指引和幫助，如何既提供優質的學習素材，又提供名師的教學方法，是當下社會關注的重要問題。針對這種情況，本館特別延請香港名校名師，根據多年豐富的教學經驗，精選海外適合初、中級英語程度讀者的優質經典讀物，有系統地出版了這套叢書，名為《Black Cat 優質英語階梯閱讀》。

　　《Black Cat 優質英語階梯閱讀》體現了香港名校名師堅持經典學習的教學理念，以及多年行之有效的學習方法。既有經過改寫和縮寫的經典名著，又有富創意的現代作品；既有精心設計的聽、説、讀、寫綜合練習，又有豐富的歷史文化知識；既有彩色插圖、繪圖和照片，又有英美專業演員朗讀作品的 CD。適合口味不同的讀者享受閱讀之樂，欣賞經典之美。

　　《Black Cat 優質英語階梯閱讀》由淺入深，逐階提升，好像參與一個尋寶遊戲，入門並不難，但要真正尋得寶藏，需要投入，更需要堅持。只有置身其中的人，才能體味純正英語的魅力，領略得到真寶的快樂。當英語閱讀成為自己生活的一部分，英語水平的提高自然水到渠成。

商務印書館（香港）有限公司
編輯部

使用説明

① 應該怎樣選書？

按閱讀興趣選書

《Black Cat 優質英語階梯閱讀》精選世界經典作品，也包括富於創意的現代作品；既有膾炙人口的小説、戲劇，又有非小説類的文化知識讀物，品種豐富，內容多樣，適合口味不同的讀者挑選自己感興趣的書，享受閱讀的樂趣。

按英語程度選書

《Black Cat 優質英語階梯閱讀》現設 Level 1 至 Level 6，由淺入深，涵蓋初、中級英語程度。讀物分級採用了國際上通用的劃分標準，主要以詞彙（vocabulary）和結構（structures）劃分。

Level 1 至 Level 3 出現的詞彙較淺顯，相對深的核心詞彙均配上中文解釋，節省讀者查找詞典的時間，以專心理解正文內容。在註釋的幫助下，讀者若能流暢地閱讀正文內容，就不用擔心這一本書程度過深。

Level 1 至 Level 3 出現的動詞時態形式和句子結構比較簡單。動詞時態形式以現在時（present simple）、現在時進行式（present continuous）、過去時（past simple）為主，句子結構大部分是簡單句（simple sentences）。此外，還包括比較級和最高級（comparative and superlative forms）、可數和不可數名詞（countable and uncountable nouns）以及冠詞（articles）等語法知識點。

Level 4 至 Level 6 出現的動詞時態形式，以現在完成時（present perfect）、現在完成時進行式（present perfect continuous）、過去完成時（past perfect continuous）為主，句子結構大部分是複合句（compound sentences）、條件從句（1st and 2nd conditional sentences）等。此外，還包括情態動詞（modal verbs）、被動形式（passive forms）、動名詞（gerunds）、

短語動詞（phrasal verbs）等語法知識點。

　　根據上述的語法範圍，讀者可按自己實際的英語水平，如詞彙量、語法知識、理解能力、閱讀能力等自主選擇，不再受制於學校年級劃分或學歷高低的約束，完全根據個人需要選擇合適的讀物。

② 怎樣提高閱讀效果？

　　閱讀的方法主要有兩種：一是泛讀，二是精讀。兩者各有功能，適當地結合使用，相輔相成，有事半功倍之效。

　　泛讀，指閱讀大量適合自己程度（可稍淺，但不能過深）、不同內容、風格、體裁的讀物，但求明白內容大意，不用花費太多時間鑽研細節，主要作用是多接觸英語，減輕對它的生疏感，鞏固以前所學過的英語，讓腦子在潛意識中吸收詞彙用法、語法結構等。

　　精讀，指小心認真地閱讀內容精彩、組織有條理、遣詞造句又正確的作品，着重點在於理解"準確"及"深入"，欣賞其精彩獨到之處。精讀時，可充分利用書中精心設計的練習，學習掌握有用的英語詞彙和語法知識。精讀後，可再花十分鐘朗讀其中一小段有趣的文字，邊唸邊細心領會文字的結構和意思。

　　《Black Cat 優質英語階梯閱讀》中的作品均值得精讀，如時間有限，不妨嘗試每兩個星期泛讀一本，輔以每星期挑選書中一章精彩的文字精讀。要學好英語，持之以恆地泛讀和精讀英文是最有效的方法。

③ 本系列的練習與測試有何功能？

　　《Black Cat 優質英語階梯閱讀》特別注重練習的設計，為讀者考慮周到，切合實用需求，學習功能強。每章後均配有訓練聽、説、讀、寫四項技能的練習，分量、難度恰到好處。

聽力練習分兩類，一是重聽故事回答問題，二是聆聽主角對話、書信朗讀、或模擬記者訪問後寫出答案，旨在以生活化的練習形式逐步提高聽力。每本書均配有 CD 提供作品朗讀，朗讀者都是專業演員，英國作品由英國演員錄音，美國作品由美國演員錄音，務求增加聆聽的真實感和感染力。多聆聽英式和美式英語兩種發音，可讓讀者熟悉二者的差異，逐漸培養分辨英美發音的能力，提高聆聽理解的準確度。此外，模仿錄音朗讀故事或模仿主人翁在戲劇中的對白，都是訓練口語能力的好方法。

閱讀理解練習形式多樣化，有縱橫字謎、配對、填空、字句重組等等，注重訓練讀者的理解、推敲和聯想等多種閱讀技能。

寫作練習尤具新意，教讀者使用網式圖示（spidergrams）記錄重點，採用問答、書信、電報、記者採訪等多樣化形式，鼓勵讀者動手寫作。

書後更設有升級測試（Exit Test）及答案，供讀者檢查學習效果。充分利用書中的練習和測試，可全面提升聽、說、讀、寫四項技能。

❹ 本系列還能提供甚麼幫助？

《Black Cat 優質英語階梯閱讀》提倡豐富多元的現代閱讀，巧用書中提供的資訊，有助於提升英語理解力，擴闊視野。

每本書都設有專章介紹相關的歷史文化知識，經典名著更有作者生平、社會背景等資訊。書內富有表現力的彩色插圖、繪圖和照片，使閱讀充滿趣味，部分加上如何解讀古典名畫的指導，增長見識。有的書還提供一些與主題相關的網址，比如關於不同國家的節慶源流的網址，讓讀者多利用網上資源增進知識。

Contents

FCE   First Certificate in English Examination-style exercises

T: GRADE 8   Trinity-Style exercises (Grade 8)

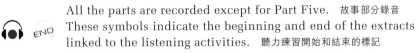

All the parts are recorded except for Part Five.　故事部分錄音
These symbols indicate the beginning and end of the extracts
linked to the listening activities.　聽力練習開始和結束的標記

Portrait of Jane Austen (*c.* 1790).

The Life of Jane Austen

Jane Austen was born on 16th December 1775 in the village of Steventon in the South of England. Her parents, an Anglican [1] clergyman [2] and his wife, a clergyman's daughter, had eight children. Jane's sister, Cassandra, was her favourite companion and they lived together or wrote to each other throughout their lives. It was normal for girls at that time to be educated at home after the age of eleven. They both read widely, learnt to play the piano, drew and learnt Italian and French.

1. **Anglican** : of the Church of England.
2. **clergyman** : a priest, somebody working in the church.

The Rectory [1] at Steventon where Jane Austen was born in 1775 in a sketch by James Edward Austen-Leigh.

The family moved to Bath in 1801. Bath was a large fashionable city with a lively social life but Jane and her sister had been happier in the small village where they were born. Jane's father died in 1805 and the two sisters moved to Southampton, a large seaport, with their mother. Three years later, however, they moved to the village of Chawton where they lived in a spacious [2] cottage. Jane lived there until she died in 1817 at the young age of forty-one. She is buried in Winchester Cathedral.

Jane's talent as a writer emerged [3] when she was still a child. She wrote stories to amuse the rest of her family. At sixteen, she wrote a comic history of the world and by the age of twenty she had written several unpublished novels.

1. **rectory** : the house of the clergyman in charge of a parish from which he receives his income directly.

2. **spacious** : big.

3. **emerged** : developed, came out.

When Jane moved to Chawton, she successfully published her novels, often developing her previous work. She never tried to become famous and her work was published anonymously [1] – 'by a lady'. *Pride and Prejudice, Sense and Sensibility, Mansfield Park, Emma* and *Persuasion* were the five great novels which she wrote in the cottage at Chawton.

Few people knew the identity of the writer of these works. However, the Prince Regent was an admirer of her stories and, at his request, she dedicated *Emma* to him. Many contemporary writers, including Sir Walter Scott, recognised that she had a 'wonderful talent'.

Her novels often reflect her life. For example, one of her brothers was adopted by a rich family, the Knights, and did not live with the Austens. In *Emma*, Frank Churchill is in the same situation. She describes the experience and feelings of upper class women very sensitively and, often, comically. [2] *Emma* contains some memorable comic characters: the dreadful snob, Mrs Elton, poor Miss Bates who cannot stop talking, Mr Elton the sentimental vicar. One critic has described her work as 'regulated [3] hatred' – she laughs at her enemies through her books and at the limitation of life in a small community.

All her novels centre on love and marriage but she is never sentimental. She suggests that a good relationship is based not only on romantic love but also on comfort, security and shared opinions. It is believed that Jane fell in love while at Bath but that her admirer died young. Later, she accepted a marriage proposal from a rich landowner but changed her mind the next morning. Unlike the heroines in her novels, she never found the man that she wanted to marry.

We learn a lot about Jane's ideas from her letters to Cassandra and to her niece, Anna. She wrote to Anna that for a novel, it was enough to write about '3 or 4 families in a country village'. This is a perfect

1. **anonymously** : with her name not made public.
2. **comically** : in an amusing way.
3. **regulated** : controlled.

description of the plot of *Emma*. Although her novels are limited in area, they express a depth of feeling and a rich sense of irony. They are still very widely read and are regularly adapted for television, the cinema or the theatre. The clergyman's daughter who preferred to live in small villages has entertained [1] the world for nearly 200 years.

In the Library, St. James' Square, by Thomas Pole.

1. **entertained** : interested and amused.

The World of Jane Austen

Jane Austen was born in the eighteenth century and died in the nineteenth. It was a time of great change in England and in the whole of Europe. The French Revolution and the Napoleonic Wars occupied most of the years of her lifetime.

For a time, many people believed that Napoleon would invade [1] the south coast of England where she lived. The Battle of Waterloo in 1815, a turning point in European history, took place two years before her death. The United States of America became independent, England became involved in war in India, there was rebellion [2] in Ireland. At the same time the Industrial Revolution was progressing rapidly. The peaceful

The Great House and Park at Chawton, by Adam Callender.

1. **invade** : enter a country with an army in order to take control of it.
2. **rebellion** : open resistance to the established government.

rural life which Jane celebrated in her novels was being threatened. [1]
Her letters show that she was keenly interested in all these developments. However, they hardly enter her novels. She prefers to describe the personal lives of characters that we all recognise from our own experience, who make mistakes, develop and come, like Emma, to a better understanding of their own hearts.

As you read *Emma*, you will read more about the world of Jane Austen.

1 **Answer the following questions.**

    a. What was Jane Austen's father's job?

    ....

    b. What kind of education did she have?

    ....

    c. Why did she start writing?

    ....

    d. What did she write before she composed her famous novels?

    ....

    e. How did she sign her novels?

    ....

    f. What are her novels mainly about?

    ....

    g. What was her opinion of love and marriage?

    ....

    h. In what important way does Jane Austen differ from the heroines of her novels?

    ....

    i. What major historic events occurred during Jane Austen's lifetime?

    ....

    j. Why are these events not mentioned in her novels?

    ....

    1. **threatened** : out in danger.

A watercolour of Jane Austen by her sister Cassandra (1804).

Before you read

FCE **1** **Listen to the beginning of Part One, and choose the correct answer (A, B or C) for each question.**

1. How old was Emma?
   - A ☐ 21.
   - B ☐ 29.
   - C ☐ 20.

2. How many brothers did she have?
   - A ☐ 2.
   - B ☐ 1.
   - C ☐ 0.

3. Who was Miss Taylor going to marry?
   - A ☐ Mr John Knightley.
   - B ☐ Mr George Knightley.
   - C ☐ Mr Weston.

4. Which one of the following was not one of the evils in Emma's life?
   - A ☐ She lived sixteen miles from London.
   - B ☐ She had been spoilt by her father and Miss Taylor.
   - C ☐ She had too high an opinion of herself.

5. Why was Emma so sad on Miss Taylor's wedding day?
   - A ☐ Because Miss Taylor's new husband's first son had been adopted by another family.
   - B ☐ Because her best friend was leaving her house.
   - C ☐ Because Miss Taylor's new husband was not an excellent man.

6. According to Emma, Miss Taylor will be much happier
   - A ☐ away from Mr Woodhouse's complaining.
   - B ☐ with her own carriage.
   - C ☐ with her own house.

Part One

The Mistress of Hartfield House

mma Woodhouse, handsome, [1] clever and rich, with a comfortable home and a happy disposition, [2] seemed to have a perfect life. She was twenty-one years old with very few problems.

Emma had one sister, Isabella, who lived in London with her husband, Mr John Knightley, and her children. Emma's mother had died while she was still very young. Since then, Miss Taylor had been Emma's governess [3] and friend for sixteen years. They were very fond of each other. But now Miss Taylor was getting

---

1. **handsome** : good-looking (a word normally used for men).
2. **disposition** : personality, character.
3. **governess** : a woman who looks after and teaches a child at home.

married to Mr Weston and would move to his house, called Randalls.

Emma lived at Hartfield, a mansion [1] on the edge of the village of Highbury. It was sixteen miles from London. The Woodhouse family was the most important family in the village. Another important family, the Knightleys, lived at Donwell Abbey, a few miles away. John Knightley's brother, Mr George Knightley, lived there. He was thirty-seven years old, unmarried, and very popular in the neighbourhood.

There were only two evils [2] in Emma's life. Firstly, she had been spoilt by her father and Miss Taylor [3] ever since her mother's death. Secondly, she had a very high opinion of herself. In fact, Emma thought that she was perfect.

It was Miss Taylor's wedding day. Emma was very sad because her best friend had left the house. Mr Weston, her new husband, was an excellent man; his first wife had died, his son had been adopted by his wife's family in the North of England, the Churchills, and he had lived alone for many years. Everyone liked

---

1. **mansion** : a large house, belonging to a wealthy person.
2. **evils** : bad things.
3. **spoilt by ... Taylor** : they had given her everything she wanted.

him. But without Miss Taylor, Emma would have no young companion in the house. She loved her father, Mr Woodhouse. But he was always worried about illness or other dangers.

'Poor Miss Taylor,' said Mr Woodhouse at every meal, while he was eating his gruel. [1] 'I wish she were here. What a pity that she married Mr Weston!'

'I cannot agree with you, papa,' said Emma. 'Miss Taylor will be far happier with her own home. We shall often visit them. We shall go in the carriage.'

'The poor horses! The poor driver!'

---

1. **gruel** : a very thin soup, supposed to be healthy.

'Don't worry. Everything is perfect.'

'Poor Miss Taylor!' said Mr Woodhouse again.

END

At that moment, Mr Knightley of Donwell Abbey came into the room.

'I have been to London,' he said, 'to visit my brother's family.'

'Poor Isabella,' said Mr Woodhouse. 'London is a very unhealthy place for her to live.'

'She and the children are all very well. Did the wedding go well?'

'Ah, poor Miss Taylor. It is a sad business.' [1]

'Nonsense!' said Mr Knightley. 'It is better to be independent.' 'Tell the truth, Mr Knightley,' said Emma, playfully. [2] 'You think it is better for Miss Taylor to escape from me and my silly imagination.'

'No, dear Emma. Perhaps I never flatter [3] you but I admire you greatly.'

'Don't forget,' said Emma, 'that I myself made the match [4] between Miss Taylor and Mr Weston. Everybody said that Mr Weston would never get married again. But I was right.'

1. **business** : (here) matter.
2. **playfully** : jokingly, humorously.
3. **flatter** : to say nice things (perhaps untrue) about somebody.
4. **made the match** : arranged the marriage, brought the couple together.

'Dear Emma, please don't make any more marriages,' said her father sadly.

'I will not get married myself, papa. But I am really successful in making matches for other people. I planned the marriage of Miss Taylor and now, dear papa, I shall plan for others.'

'Nonsense!' said Mr Knightley. 'Miss Taylor and Mr Weston decided themselves to get married. You did nothing. You just made a lucky guess.' [1]

'I encouraged Mr Weston to visit Hartfield and meet Miss Taylor. I played an important part.'

'It is a dangerous thing to do, Emma. Don't interfere in [2] other people's lives.'

'Dear Emma is so kind. She always thinks about others,' said Mr Woodhouse affectionately.

'Mr Elton, the vicar, [3] needs a wife. I will look for one for him,' declared Emma.

Mr Knightley laughed. 'He is twenty-seven years old. He can find his own wife if he wants one. Oh Emma, be serious.'

Mr and Mrs Weston, Mr Knightley and Mr Elton, the vicar, often came to visit Mr Woodhouse. They also came, of course, to talk with his lovely daughter.

There was another group of visitors. Mrs Bates was a very old lady. Her daughter, Miss Bates, was middle-aged but single. She devoted her life to caring for her mother. Miss Bates was famous for talking too much and saying stupid things. But she was so

---

1. **made a lucky guess** : knew something by luck.
2. **interfere in** : get involved in a situation where you are not wanted or needed.
3. **vicar** : the man in charge of a church, an Anglican priest.

kind and generous that nobody disliked her. Mrs Goddard, their friend, was the headmistress [1] of the village school.

One evening, they brought Harriet Smith, an orphan, with them to meet Emma and Mr Woodhouse. Harriet was a very pretty girl, about eighteen. She was short, plump [2] and fair with blue eyes. Nobody knew who her parents had been. She lived at the school.

Emma immediately liked Harriet Smith. She was sweet, shy and very grateful for the invitation to Hartfield. 'I can help this girl,' thought Emma. 'I can give her knowledge and good manners. [3] She isn't clever but she has soft eyes and a beautiful appearance.'

Emma invited Harriet more and more to Hartfield. She enjoyed helping and influencing her. Little by little, Harriet shyly told her about herself.

'Last summer, I stayed with the Martins at Abbey Mill Farm on Mr Knightley's estate. [4] They were very kind to me. They have eight cows on their farm!'

---

1. **headmistress** : a female teacher who is in charge of a school.
2. **plump** : pleasingly fat.
3. **good manners** : polite ways of behaving in society.
4. **estate** : a large area of land belonging to a gentleman.

The Mistress of Hartfield House

Emma, the mistress of Hartfield House, was not interested in cows. But when she found out that Harriet had met Mr Martin, the unmarried son of the family, she became worried.

'He came with us on our moonlit [1] walks. Once, he rode three miles to get me some walnuts. [2] He is very clever and has a fine flock [3] of sheep. His mother says that he will make a fine husband.'

Emma did not like this story. She wanted to improve Harriet. Emma did not want her to be in love with an uneducated farmer!

'What does Mr Martin look like?' asked Emma.

'He's not handsome. But I like him. Haven't you seen him? He often rides through Highbury.'

'I don't notice young farmers,' said Emma snobbishly. [4] 'How old is he?'

'Twenty-four.'

'Ah, he is much too young to get married. He must wait at least six years until he has enough money.'

'Six years, Miss Woodhouse!' exclaimed Harriet. 'But he'll be thirty!!!'

Next day, they met Mr Martin when they were out walking. He looked very happy to see Harriet. Emma thought that he was neat [5] and looked sensible [6] but he was not handsome.

When he had gone, Harriet came running back to Emma with a smiling face.

'It was so lucky to meet him. What do you think of him, Miss

---

1. **moonlit** : lit by the moon.
2. **walnuts** : a kind of nut.
3. **flock** : a group of animals, such as birds, sheep.
4. **snobbishly** : proudly.
5. **neat** : having a tidy and pleasing appearance.
6. **sensible** : with practical intelligence.

Woodhouse?'

'He is very plain [1] – remarkably plain. And he is clearly not a gentleman. He has no manners.'

Harriet was very disappointed. 'Of course,' she said sadly, 'he is not as genteel [2] as a real gentleman.'

'I think, Harriet, since you have known me, you have been in the company of real gentlemen. I should be surprised if you can still like Mr Martin.'

'Certainly he is not like Mr Knightley. But Mr Knightley is a very fine man.'

'True, Mr Knightley is one in a hundred. And Mr Elton is also an example of a very fine gentleman. In fact, I think that Mr Elton likes you, Harriet.'

'Oh, Miss Woodhouse! Do you think so?' And Harriet seemed to have completely forgotten Mr Martin, the young farmer. Emma congratulated herself. She was the perfect match-maker. [3]

Meanwhile, Mr Knightley was talking to Mrs Weston about Emma. 'I think this friendship between Emma and Harriet Smith is a bad thing, Mrs Weston.'

'A bad thing! Why? I am very pleased to see them together,' replied Mrs Weston. 'To educate Harriet, Emma will read more herself.'

'Emma always plans to read more. I have seen all the lists of books she made when she was twelve years old. But she is never hard-working or patient. Her imagination is stronger than her

---

1. **plain** : ordinary, not handsome or attractive.
2. **genteel** : with good manners, like a gentleman or lady.
3. **match-maker** : someone who finds husbands or wives for others.

understanding. Her father spoils her. And since her mother died, she has been the mistress ¹ of Hartfield and the mistress of you all!'

'But she is so happy to have a friend of her own age. She looks very well.'

'Yes, Emma is very pretty.'

'Pretty, Mr Knightley! She is perfect beauty,' said Mrs Weston.

'Well, I confess that I have seldom seen anyone more attractive. But I am an old friend. She always says that she will never marry. It would do her good to be in love. But there is no-one in Highbury to attract her.'

Mrs Weston smiled mysteriously. Would Emma fall in love with Frank Churchill, Mr Weston's son, if he came to Highbury? It would be the perfect marriage.

---

1. **she has ... mistress** : she has had control.

Go back to the text

FCE **1** **Choose from the characters (A-D) to answer the questions. There is an example at the beginning.**

A Emma

B Mr George Knightley

C Mr Woodhouse

D Harriet Smith

Who:

0. | C | seems to be always worried about almost everything?

1. | | has a brother who lives in London?

2. | | feels that he/she is responsible for Mr and Mrs Weston's marriage?

3. | | thinks that Emma should not try to direct other people's lives?

4. | | wants to find a wife for Mr Elton?

5. | | is an orphan?

6. | | admires Mr Martin?

7. | | thinks that Mr Martin is not rich enough to get married?

8. | | admires Emma but thinks that she is spoilt?

9. | | thinks that Emma is a good person because she is always trying to help others?

10. | | believes that he/she will never get married?

2 **What do you think? Why?**

a. Will Emma have a good influence on Harriet?

b. Will Frank Churchill play an important part in the story?

c. Will Emma fall in love?

d. Will Mr and Mrs Weston have a happy marriage?

Reporting conversations

Often, we need to report a conversation. We want to give the information some time after the original conversation took place. Look at this example from the story:

*Everybody said that Mr Weston **would** never **get married** again.*
Originally, people said: *'He **will** never **get married** again.'*

In reported speech, the verb goes one step back in the past. Here are some more examples. Study the changes.

*'I **am going** to travel to London **tomorrow**.'*
*He said that he **was going** to travel to London **the next day**.*

*'My sister **has fallen** in love with a soldier.'*
*She told me that **her** sister **had fallen** in love with a soldier.*

*'I **came here** yesterday to see you,' he told her.*
*He said that he **had gone there** the previous day to see her.*

*'**Did** you **go** to the party?'*
*He asked her if she **had gone** to the party.*

3 **Put these sentences into either direct or reported speech.**

    a. Emma said that she would come to see me.

    b. Mr Knightley said, 'I have been to London to visit my brother's family.'

    c. 'I myself made the match,' stated Emma.

    d. Mr Woodhouse said that he was very sad about the wedding.

    e. 'It is a dangerous thing to do,' Mr Woodhouse told Emma.

    f. Mr Weston said that they had gone to London for the holidays.

    g. Emma declared, 'I will look for a wife for Mr Elton.'

    h. He told me that Miss Taylor was getting married.

    i. Harriet told her that she had stayed with the Martins last summer.

    j. Harriet exclaimed, 'I was so lucky to meet him.'

Writing

4 **Write a report of the conversation among Emma, Mr Knightley and Mr Woodhouse (pp. 20-21). You can begin like this:**

At that moment, Mr Knightley of Donwell Abbey came into the room. He said that he had been to London to visit his brother's family. Mr Woodhouse felt sorry for Isabella as he thought that London was a very unhealthy place for her to live. However, Mr Knightley...

Now imagine a conversation among three neighbours about some local news, for example:

– a murder

– a marriage

– a dramatic love affair

– an accident

– a plan for a new hospital

Write a report of the conversation. For example:

Mr Brown said that the police had found a man's body in the lake. Mrs Smith asked how old the man was. Mr Brown said that he was about twenty. Mrs Baxter told them that she had heard a strange noise in the middle of the previous night...

Thinking

T: GRADE 8

5 **Topic – Living standards**
Ask a relative (grandparents, aunt, uncle etc.) about how they lived when they were young. Use an old photo of them and think about how they lived in the past.
Use the following questions to help you:

a. When was the photo taken? What was this relative doing at that time?

b. Where were they living? What was their house like?

c. What type of work did most people do?

d. What one thing has changed most in their life since the photo was taken?

Characters

6 Mr Woodhouse is always worried about other people. He seems very unselfish. But, as you can already see, he doesn't like people to be independent. For example, he doesn't want Miss Taylor to be married and to leave Hartfield.

Imagine a modern Mr Woodhouse. Choose some of the following situations and write a dialogue(s) between Mr Woodhouse and his daughter.

– Emma wants to go away to university in the USA.
– She has fallen in love and wants to get married.
– She wants to go on holiday to Africa.
– She wants to meet a friend in the pub.
– She wants to take a well-paid job in another town.

For example, you can begin like this:

Emma: Dad, I've been offered a place at university in California. Isn't it great?

Dad: It's a very long way away. You might be unhappy living in America.

Emma: No, it'll be really exciting.

Dad: But American food is very unhealthy. All the Americans are fat. Stay at home and let me cook for you.

Emma: But Dad,...

For questions 1-12, read the text below and decide which answer (A, B, C or D) best fits each space. There is an example at the beginning.

Jane Austen at Chawton

Jane Austen moved to Chawton **(0)** <u>A</u> July, 1809. Her brother Edward, who had been adopted by the rich Knight family, **(1)** ....
to renovate a cottage there in the small village. It is now **(2)** .... to visit the house and see it as it was when Jane lived there. She used to write at a small table. There was a creaking door. When Jane heard the noise of the door, she knew that she had visitors and she hid the **(3)** .... of her novels. She was a very private person!

The vicar of Chawton was a middle-aged bachelor, and a friend **(4)** .... that Jane should marry him. Jane laughed

Chawton Cottage.

(**5**) .... this. In fact, she was happy living with her mother and beloved sister, Cassandra, and her books, (**6**) .... she called 'my children'. Jane's brothers often visited and she (**7**) .... a close friendship with one of her nieces, Anna. The girl wanted to be a novelist and sent examples of her work to her aunt. This probably helped Jane to rediscover her enthusiasm for writing. She found her first publisher in 1811. In 1815, *Emma* was published. Two thousand copies were printed (**8**) .... not all of them were sold. She (**9**) .... a profit of £39!

Obviously, Jane's reputation was (**10**) .... slowly. She never personally met (**11**) .... other author, and did not go to London to promote her writing.

When Jane's health suddenly (**12**) .... worse – she probably had 'Addison's Disease' – she moved briefly to Winchester in order to consult an experienced doctor. He could not save her, however, and on July 18th, 1817, she died in the arms of Cassandra.

0.	**A** in	**B** at	**C** on	**D** for
1.	**A** offered	**B** presented	**C** ordered	**D** said
2.	**A** likely	**B** possible	**C** probable	**D** feasible
3.	**A** writings	**B** papers	**C** manuscripts	**D** documents
4.	**A** suggested	**B** wanted	**C** considered	**D** told
5.	**A** to	**B** for	**C** in	**D** at
6.	**A** what	**B** who	**C** which	**D** whose
7.	**A** gave	**B** made	**C** did	**D** formed
8.	**A** but	**B** as	**C** still	**D** while
9.	**A** collected	**B** did	**C** made	**D** took
10.	**A** worsening	**B** becoming	**C** raising	**D** growing
11.	**A** any	**B** some	**C** an	**D** one
12.	**A** took	**B** got	**C** was	**D** turned

Before you go on

FCE **1** Listen to the beginning of Part Two, and identify the correct character (A-D).

A Emma   **B** Mr Elton

C Harriet Smith   **D** Mr Knightley

Who:

1. ☐ wants Emma to paint Harriet's picture?
2. ☐ criticises the picture?
3. ☐ thinks that Emma is a very good artist?
4. ☐ is certain that Mr Elton is in love with Harriet?
5. ☐ receives a letter?
6. ☐ offers Harriet advice?
7. ☐ would be very sad if he/she could never visit Emma again?
8. ☐ thinks Mr Martin wants to marry Harriet for social reasons alone?
9. ☐ thinks that Mr Martin is Harriet's social equal?
10. ☐ thinks that Emma has been match-making?

2 **What do you think? Why?**

a. Do you agree more with Emma or Mr Knightley as regards to Mr Martin's proposal?

b. Would you have agreed to marry Mr Martin if you had been Harriet?

Part Two

Match-Maker or Trouble-Maker?

mma had decided to make a match between Mr Elton and Harriet Smith. Emma was sure that Mr Elton was already half in love with her.

'You have given Harriet so much,' he told her. 'You have made her graceful and elegant, Miss Woodhouse.'

'Thank you, Mr Elton.'

'Let me ask you to paint her picture, Miss Woodhouse. You are a talented artist.'

Harriet was very shy but she agreed to sit for her portrait. [1] Emma took out her water colours and began to work. Mr Elton sat near her, constantly [2] jumping up to look at the picture.

---

1. **portrait** : a painting of a person.
2. **constantly** : always, continuously.

'That is an excellent likeness.' [1]

'Thank you, Mr Elton,' said Emma. 'He must be very much in love with her, I have only just begun,' she thought.

'Harriet is not as beautiful as that,' said Mr Weston arriving to see Mr Woodhouse.

'You have made her too tall,' said Mr Knightley.

'Poor Harriet,' said Mr Woodhouse, 'you are painting her outdoors. She will catch cold.'

'Oh no,' said Mr Elton. 'It is a perfect work of art. I will ride to London to have it framed.' [2]

Emma was very pleased. Mr Elton was obviously in love. But next day, Harriet came to Hartfield soon after breakfast.

'What is the matter?' asked Emma.

'Mr Martin has written to me. He has asked me to marry him.'

'He wants to have good connections,' [3] said Emma coldly.

'Please, read the letter. It is a very good letter.'

Emma was surprised to find that the letter was short but well written.

1. **likeness** : similarity, a recognisable painting of someone.

2. **framed** : put in a wooden frame.

3. **good connections** : friends or relatives from a high social class.

'But what shall I do?' asked Harriet.

'You ought to write politely but firmly like a lady. Thank him for his offer but explain that it is impossible.'

'I had no idea that he liked me so much. Do you think that it is better to say no, Miss Woodhouse?'

'You must make your own decision.'

'Then perhaps I ought to refuse him.'

'Perfectly right, Harriet. If you were married to a farmer, I could never visit you. It would be socially [1] impossible.'

'Oh, Miss Woodhouse, I couldn't bear it. [2] It would have killed me never to come to Hartfield again.'

'Dear, sweet, little friend,' said Emma. 'Let me help you write your answer.'

The letter was sent.

'Poor Mr Martin,' said Harriet sadly.

'You will always be welcome here at Hartfield. And remember Mr Elton. At this moment he is in London. Perhaps he is showing your portrait to his mother and sisters.'

'Oh, Miss Woodhouse, do you think so?'

Next day, Mr Knightley called on [3] Emma. He was very angry when he found out that Harriet had refused Mr Martin. 'The girl

1. **socially** : in society.
2. **bear it** : accept it, tolerate it.
3. **called on** : paid a visit to, came to see.

is a fool. Emma, is this your work? Did you persuade her to refuse him?'

'How can she accept him? He is not her equal.' [1]

'Not Harriet's equal! Harriet is pretty and kind but that is all. Robert Martin is sensible, sincere and is a natural gentleman.'

'Anyway,' said Emma, 'Harriet has a different destiny.' [2]

END

'Are you match-making?' asked Mr Knightley. 'Well, if Mr Elton is a part of your plan, then you are making a great mistake.' He left angrily.

Mr Elton brought back the picture from London and they hung it in the main room.

'It is a beautiful painting,' he sighed.

Harriet was busy writing out riddles [3] in a book. It was a fashionable thing for young ladies to do, to copy clever pieces of literature.

'Why don't you write a riddle for us, Mr Elton?' asked Emma.

'I'm not clever enough,' he said but next day he arrived with a piece of paper. He gave it to Emma.

When he had gone, Emma and Harriet read it together. [4]

'In my first, rich kings live at ease...'

'That means "court",' [5] thought Emma.

'My second is the monarch of the seas...'

'That means "ship",' thought Emma.

---

1. **equal** : person equal to someone else in some way.
2. **destiny** : that which happens to someone.
3. **riddles** : clever puzzles using words.
4. **Mr Elton's riddle** : some of the language is difficult. Don't worry if you don't understand everything!
5. **court** : two meanings – 'a king's palace' and 'to want to marry a girl'.

'But ah! united, all man's freedom is flown;
 And woman, lovely woman, reigns [1] alone...'
'That means "courtship",' [2] thought Emma.
'Your ready wit [3] the word will soon supply.
May its approval smile in that soft eye!'
'That is Harriet's "soft eye",' thought Emma.
'I don't understand,' said Harriet. 'What does it mean? 'Monarch of the seas'? Is that a mermaid? Or a shark?'

'Mermaids and sharks! Nonsense! My dear Harriet, the answer is 'courtship'. It is written for you. I congratulate you with all my heart. Here is proof that Mr Elton loves you.'

'Dear Miss Woodhouse,' said Harriet. 'Oh, Mr Elton is a true gentleman like Mr Knightley.'

That evening, Mr Elton called again.

'Thank you for the riddle,' said Emma. 'I have written it in Miss Smith's book.'

'That is an honour, Miss Woodhouse,' said Mr Elton gallantly. [4] 'It is the proudest moment of my life.'

Next day, Emma was walking in the village with Harriet.

'One day, Harriet, you will live in the vicarage. [5] And I shall come and visit you.'

'And I shall visit you, Miss Woodhouse, when you are married.'

'No, I shall never marry. I have never been in love because I have never met a superior [6] man. I am content [7] to live in my father's

---

1. **reigns** : has power, governs.
2. **courtship** : the time when a man and a woman are in love, leading to marriage.
3. **ready wit** : quick intelligence.
4. **gallantly** : in a way that shows special attention and respect to women.
5. **vicarage** : the house where the vicar lives.
6. **superior** : better than average.
7. **content** : satisfied, happy.

house. It is a perfect life.'

They went to the cottage [1] of a poor family of the village. Emma went inside to talk to the sick children and to offer advice and sympathy. Walking on, they met Mr Elton in the lane. [2] He walked with them until they reached the vicarage. 'Harriet must go inside,' thought Emma. 'I have an idea!'

She stopped and pretended to tie her boot lace. [3] While no one was looking at her, she broke the lace and threw it away.

'Oh!' she cried, 'part of my lace is missing. Mr Elton, may I stop at your house and ask your house-keeper for help?'

'Dear Miss Woodhouse. Please come inside. Oh, and Miss Smith too.'

Inside the house, Emma asked the housekeeper to mend [4] her boot, leaving Mr Elton and Harriet alone in the next room. 'Perhaps he will ask her to marry him!'

But Emma was disappointed. He said nothing.

1. **cottage** : a small house, usually in a village.
2. **lane** : a small road or path.
3. **lace** : a string to tie shoes.
4. **mend** : repair.

Isabella, Mr John Knightley, their five children and their nursemaids [1] came to Hartfield for Christmas. One evening they talked about the Westons.

'But has Mr Weston's son come to visit them since the wedding?' asked John.

When Mr Weston's first wife had died, their son, Frank Churchill, had gone to live with his wealthy aunt and uncle in the North of England, in Yorkshire. He was now twenty-three years old but his aunt, Mrs Churchill, was a proud, stubborn [2] old lady. She made it difficult for Frank to visit his father at Highbury.

'No,' answered Emma. 'He has written a letter promising to visit but he has not yet come here. All of Highbury wants to see him.'

Later, Mr Knightley joined them for dinner.

Emma was holding Isabella's baby daughter in her arms. He came up to her and she passed the child to him.

'At least we can agree about our baby niece,' [3] she said. 'We both think that she is charming.'

'If you judged adults as well as you judge children, we would always agree,' he smiled.

'I hope that Mr Martin is not too disappointed.'

---

1. **nursemaids** : servants to look after young children.
2. **stubborn** : determined not to give way.
3. **niece** : the daughter of a brother or sister.

'A man could not be more disappointed.'

'I am very sorry,' said Emma sincerely. 'But come, shake hands with me.'

They were friends again.

Later that evening, they decided that they would all visit Randalls on Christmas Eve. Mr Elton and Harriet would be invited too. Unfortunately, Harriet developed a sore throat. [1] Emma told Mr Elton, 'She is too ill to come to the party.'

'Be careful, Miss Woodhouse. Do not catch the infection from her.'

'But you must be careful too, Mr Elton. Don't come out in the cold weather. Remember, you must preach [2] on Christmas Day.'

'Thank you. The advice of such a beautiful lady is precious to me. But I am looking forward to the party.'

'How strange!' Emma thought. 'The woman he loves is ill but he still smiles.'

'Be careful, Emma,' said Mr John Knightley. 'I think Mr Elton is in love with you. I have been watching him.'

'With me? What an idea! You are quite mistaken!'

1. **a sore throat** : an infection that makes it painful to talk.
2. **preach** : give a talk on a religious subject.

Go back to the text

FCE **1** **Choose the correct answer (A, B, C or D) for each question.**

1. What are some of the reasons why Emma believes that Mr Elton is in love with Harriet?

   A ☐ Because Harriet has become so socially elegant and attractive.

   B ☐ Because he asks Emma to paint Harriet's portrait and he writes a riddle about her.

   C ☐ Because she knows that Mr Elton knows that Harriet would be the perfect wife for a vicar.

   D ☐ Because he certainly realises that Emma is his superior and would never marry him.

2. How did Emma have Harriet invited into the vicarage?

   A ☐ She decided to pass by the vicarage with Harriet in the hope of seeing Mr Elton.

   B ☐ She told Harriet to pretend to have a sore throat.

   C ☐ She asked Mr Elton to write a riddle for Harriet.

   D ☐ She broke her boot lace so they could be invited into the vicarage.

3. Why was Emma disappointed with the visit?

   A ☐ Because she had to trick Mr Elton to get invited.

   B ☐ Because she knew that Mr Knightley would not approve of their visit.

   C ☐ Because she realised during their visit that Mr Elton wanted to marry Harriet just to improve his social connections.

   D ☐ Because Mr Elton did not ask Harriet to get married during their visit.

4. Who is Frank Churchill?

   A ☐ He is a friend of the Westons.

   B ☐ He is Mrs Weston's son.

   C ☐ He is Mrs Churchill's nephew.

   D ☐ He is John's son by a first marriage.

5. What do Mr Knightley and Emma agree about?

   A ☐ That Harriet shouldn't marry Mr Elton.

   B ☐ That their niece is charming.

   C ☐ That Emma is good at judging adults.

   D ☐ That Harriet should marry Mr Martin.

6. How does Mr Elton react to the news that Harriet is ill?

   A ☐ He is worried that she might infect Emma.

   B ☐ He is worried about her.

   C ☐ He is worried that there will be no party.

   D ☐ He is worried that she might infect him.

2 What do you think? Why?

   a. Will the party at Randalls be successful?

   b. Will Mr Elton marry Harriet?

   c. Will Frank visit Highbury in January?

   d. Will Mr Martin forget Harriet?

Having something done

Mr Elton said: '*I will ride to London and have the picture framed.*' He means that somebody else will frame the picture for him. It isn't important who frames the picture.

HAVE	+	OBJECT	+	PAST PARTICIPLE
I will have		*the picture*		*framed*

Here are some more examples:

*Frank Churchill **has had** his hair **cut**.*
*Isabella **had** her children **looked after** by a nursemaid.*

In spoken English we can also use **get** instead of **have**:

*I will **get** the picture **framed**.   He is **getting** his hair **cut**.*

Notice how both **get** and **have** change tense as appropriate.

3 **Rewrite the following sentences using the words in brackets.**

   a. A photographer is taking his picture. *(get)*

   b. I will pay a painter to paint my house. *(have)*

   c. A technician repaired our computer last week. *(get)*

   d. A dentist has removed her wisdom teeth. *(have)*

   e. A mechanic services my car every six months. *(get)*

4 **Now complete the following sentences using 'get/have something done' with one of the verbs below.**

     shorten   lengthen   test   cut   install   fill   ~~deliver~~

Example:

They must have these books by tomorrow, but I have to stay here. I ***will have*** *them* ***delivered***.

   a. I had a terrible toothache because I had a large cavity. So, I went to the dentist and ....

   b. This coat was too long but I .... Now it fits perfectly.

   c. I don't like long hair. In fact, every three weeks I ....

   d. My eyes hurt, and I keep getting headaches. I think I ....

   e. I know nothing about computers. Every time I need a programme I ....

   f. These trousers fit you perfectly, except they are a bit too short. You should ....

44

Writing

 5 Pretend you are Harriet. Write a letter to an old friend in which you explain what happened with Mr Martin. Use between 120 and 180 words.

Include the following information:

- who Mr Martin is
- how you met him
- who Emma Woodhouse is and what she thinks of him
- what Mr Martin asked you
- how you responded
- any doubts you may have about your decision

Start and finish your letter like this:

Dearest Sarah,

Do you remember how we used to talk together about marriage when we were in the orphanage together. Well, you won't believe it but...

Your old and still loyal friend,
Harriet Smith

6 What do you think? Why?

- **a.** Are boys more romantic than girls?
- **b.** If someone is in love, do they always use fine words?
- **c.** Do girls like to be told they're beautiful?
- **d.** Do boys like to be told they're handsome?
- **e.** Is it sometimes right for a third person to help two people to fall in love? Has it ever happened to you?

Jane Austen and Reading

Jane Austen loved reading. She believed in the great importance of literature and wrote that it showed 'the greatest power of the human mind.' She was familiar with the classic authors such as Shakespeare but also kept up-to-date with [1] the latest writers. She also knew the dangers of literature. There was a fashion for very dramatic, romantic novels by authors such as Mrs Radcliffe. In her early novel, *Northanger Abbey,* Jane laughs at her heroine who expects life to be as exciting as one of these novels. *Emma* continues this idea of the dangers of the imagination. Emma Woodhouse behaves as if life is a love story which she can control. As Mr Knightley says, she has 'more imagination than understanding'.

A manuscript [2] written by Jane Austen at the age of 16.

1. **kept up-to-date with** : knew about what was happening.
2. **manuscript** : the first copy of a piece of writing written by hand.

There is little reference to literature in *Emma*. Mr Knightley remembers that Emma has made many lists of good books but that she has failed to read them. Emma plans to educate Harriet by giving her a programme of reading but, in fact, they are always thinking too much about love to have time for literature!

The newest movement in European literature and art at this time was known as Romanticism. Many famous English writers belong to this period – Byron, Shelley, Keats, Walter Scott. The Romantics generally preferred passion and imagination to calmness and reason. [1] They also preferred the wild dramatic landscape of the Lake District in northern England or the Alps in Switzerland. In most ways, Jane Austen does not share these ideas although she lived and wrote at the same time. In *Emma*, she praises the calm, sweet English countryside at Donwell Abbey and Box Hill.

A View of Box Hill (1816), by Humphrey Repton.

1.   **reason** : (here) power of the mind to think and understand.

There are no passionate and dramatic incidents in the novel. Instead there is wit [1] and irony [2] and a deep understanding of human behaviour.

1 **Decide if the following statements are true (T) or false (F). Then correct the false ones.**

		T	F
a.	Jane Austen thought that literature was the greatest power of the human mind.	☐	☐
b.	She read only the classics of English literature.	☐	☐
c.	*Northanger Abbey* is a wildly romantic novel by Mrs Radcliffe.	☐	☐
d.	Her novel *Emma* speaks very little of literature.	☐	☐
e.	Jane Austen was a typical representative of the English Romantic movement in literature.	☐	☐
f.	Romantic writers had a great dislike of wild landscapes.	☐	☐
g.	She thought that an uncontrolled belief in imagination could create problems.	☐	☐
h.	In her novels she paid tribute to England's rural areas.	☐	☐
i.	Her novels are characterised by a good knowledge of human nature.	☐	☐

Before you go on

1 **What do you think? Why?**

Mr Knightley says that Emma has more imagination than understanding. How is Emma's relationship with Harriet true to this?

1. **wit** : intelligent humour.
2. **irony** : using words that are the opposite of what they really mean.

Part Three

The Great Mistake

t was Christmas Eve. The carriages were ready in the courtyard at Hartfield, and Emma travelled in the second one with Mr John Knightley. It was already beginning to snow. At the vicarage, Mr Elton joined them. He seemed extremely happy. She did not understand – his loved one was ill.

They entered Randalls. Mr Weston was talking about 'Mr Frank Churchill'. Emma found that the name had a strange effect on her feelings. She was inexplicably [1] excited.

Frank would visit Highbury in January. Emma had never met Frank Churchill but she had frequently thought that, if she ever married, he was the most suitable person in age, character and social position. Their families were connected. He seemed to belong to her.

'We are not sure that Frank will come,' said Mrs Weston later.

---

1. **inexplicably** : that can not be explained.

'His aunt may refuse to allow him. The Churchills think that the Westons are below them.' [1]

'You told me that he was in Weymouth [2] in the autumn. Then surely he can find time to visit his father,' said Emma.

'He is his aunt's favourite. She will find a way to keep him in Yorkshire.'

Standing beside her, Mr Elton began (2) talking to Emma. 'You must promise me, Miss Woodhouse, not to see Harriet again until she is well. You must not put yourself in danger of becoming ill yourself. Don't you agree with me, Mrs Weston?'

Emma gave him an angry look. He was talking as if he had the right of first interest in her.

At that moment, Mr John (3) Knightley came into the room. 'There is a snowstorm outside. The roads may be blocked. [3] We may not be able to get back tonight.'

'Oh, the poor horses. What shall we do, my dear Emma,' cried Mr Woodhouse.

'My children are at Hartfield,' said Isabella.

Mr Knightley had kept calm. He went out to examine the road and returned. 'There is no difficulty,' he reported. 'There is very little snow on the ground and the clouds are already clearing.' [4]

---

1. **below them** : socially inferior.
2. **Weymouth** : a fashionable holiday town on the coast.
3. **blocked** : made impossible for traffic.
4. **clearing** : disappearing.

The Great Mistake

But Mr Woodhouse was so worried that they decided to leave immediately. They all went out to the carriages. Mr Woodhouse and Isabella got in the first carriage. In the confusion, Mr John Knightley joined them, forgetting that he was travelling with Emma. She got in the second carriage and found Mr Elton following her. The coachman shut the door. They were alone together. And Mr Elton had been drinking Mr Weston's red wine.

As soon as the carriage passed through the gates, Mr Elton seized [1] her hand.

'You know that I love you. I am ready to die for you. Please accept me as your husband.'

'I am very much astonished, [2] Mr Elton. You are in love with Miss Smith. How can you say these words to me?'

'Miss Smith! I have never been interested in Miss Smith. It is you I love, dear Miss Woodhouse. Say that you will marry me.'

'For the past month you have been courting Miss Smith. You took her portrait to London, you wrote a riddle for her, you

---

1. **seized** : took violently.
2. **astonished** : very surprised.

visited her at Hartfield constantly... This is very bad behaviour, Mr Elton.'

'Good heavens!' cried Mr Elton. 'I never ever thought of Miss Smith. She is a penniless [1] orphan. Everything I have said and done has been for you. I am sure that you understood.'

Emma was coldly silent.

But Mr Elton tried to seize her hand again.

'Charming Miss Woodhouse, do not be shy. Confess that you return my affections.'

'No sir,' cried Emma, 'I have always thought that you loved my friend. I could never consider marrying you.'

Mr Elton was silent. He sat angrily in his corner of the carriage while Emma sat angrily in hers. The carriage went slowly through the snow. The journey was like torture [2] for them. Mr Elton jumped out as soon as they arrived at the vicarage.

'Goodnight!' said Emma.

'Goodnight!' he replied coldly and proudly.

(5) The carriage drove on to Hartfield. Emma was feeling very miserable. 'How shall I tell Harriet? I have been only half a friend to her.'

Isabella and John returned to London soon after Christmas. Mr Elton wrote to Mr Woodhouse. 'I am going to Bath [3] for a few weeks to spend some time with friends.'

Harriet of course was heart-broken. There was more bad news. Frank Churchill wrote that he could not come to Highbury. 'My aunt cannot spare [4] me.'

1. **penniless** : poor, with no money.
2. **torture** : great suffering.
3. **Bath** : a city in the West of England, very fashionable in Jane Austen's time.
4. **spare** : be without.

The Great Mistake

Mr Knightley was furious. 'He must be a very proud, selfish young man to treat his father in this way.'

'But he depends on the Churchills. You are independent, you cannot understand his situation. When he finally comes to Hartfield, I shall welcome him. We do not often see fine young men, well-bred [1] and fashionable.'

'My dear Emma, he is a spoilt puppy!' [2]

Emma and Harriet went to visit Miss Bates.

Miss Bates began talking at once and did not stop. 'I have had a long letter from Jane, my niece.'

Jane Fairfax was an orphan. Her father had been killed in the war overseas and her mother had died soon afterwards. Fortunately, she had been brought up by her father's friend, Colonel Campbell, and his wife. She was a companion for their daughter who had just got married to Mr Dixon, a rich young man. The Campbells lived in Weymouth but Mr Dixon had taken his new bride to live in Ireland with him. As Jane had no wealth of her own, she now had to leave the Campbell family and find a job as a governess. But first, she would come to Highbury and stay with her aunt.

'Jane will miss Mr and Mrs Dixon. Mr Dixon once saved her from drowning, you know.'

---

1. **well-bred** : well educated, with good manners.
2. **puppy** : a young dog, used to mean an irresponsible young man.

Emma's imagination began to work. 'I wonder if Jane is in love with Mr Dixon. Perhaps that is why she is coming here, to escape a broken heart.'

Emma had not seen Jane Fairfax for two years. 'You envy [1] her,' Mr Knightley once said. 'She is a really talented young woman.' Yes, Jane could play the piano, sing and draw better than Emma. But also she was cold and reserved. [2]

As soon as Jane arrived, Emma went to visit her. She liked her better. She was elegant, with more beauty in her face than Emma remembered. Her eyes were deep grey, with dark eyelashes [3] and eyebrows; [4] her skin was clear and delicate. [5] She seemed ill.

'Perhaps she is heart-broken for Mr Dixon,' imagined Emma.

Then Jane visited Hartfield with her aunt. Miss Bates talked without stopping about Jane's talents and her health. Then both Emma and Jane played the piano but Jane was clearly more talented.

'Did you meet Frank Churchill when you were in Weymouth?' asked Emma. 'Is he handsome?'

'Yes, I met him. But I hardly remember him.'

'She is so cold, so reserved,' thought Emma. 'I don't like her after all. Harriet will continue to be my first friend.'

Next day, Mr Knightley called at Hartfield.

'I was so pleased to see that you and Jane Fairfax were friends last night,' he said to Emma. 'It was kind of you to let her play at the piano – she has no piano at Miss Bates's house.'

---

1. **envy** : be jealous, want to be in someone else's position.
2. **reserved** : slow to show feelings or express opinions.
3. **eyelashes** : the hairs around the eyes.
4. **eyebrows** : the hairs on the forehead above the eyes.
5. **delicate** : soft, tender.

(8)   At that moment, Miss Bates and Jane themselves entered. Miss Bates could not wait to give the latest news.

'Mr Elton is going to be married! He has met Miss Hawkins at Bath. She comes from a rich trading [1] family. It is a very good match.'

'Poor Harriet,' thought Emma immediately.

'Poor Mr Elton. He is very young to get married,' said Mr Woodhouse.

Emma had to tell Harriet the news. Luckily, Harriet had just met Mr Martin and his sister in the village shop. They had talked kindly to her. She did not care so much about Mr Elton.

'It was all my mistake,' thought Emma. 'But Harriet is too good to be a farmer's wife. I must try to help her.'

---

1. **trading** : buying and selling, business.

Go back to the text

1 **Part Three has been divided into eight sections. Choose the most suitable heading from the list (A-I) for each section. There is one extra heading which you do not need to use.**

A ☐ Imagination meets reality.
B ☐ That man's mine.
C ☐ She loves me? She loves me not!
D ☐ Take good care of yourself, you belong to me.
E ☐ Difficult travelling conditions.
F ☐ No parents, no money? Get a job!
G ☐ Real love means real patience.
H ☐ Two women disappointed in love.
I ☐ Artistic she is, sociable she isn't.

2 **What do you think? Why?**

a. What clues did Emma have that Mr Elton was in love with her and not with Harriet?
b. What does Emma's inability to interpret these clues correctly tell us about Emma?
c. How does Emma feel about Mr Churchill? Why does she feel this way?
d. How does Emma feel about Jane? Why does she feel this way?
e. How does Mr Knightley react to Emma's defence of Frank Churchill?
f. Does Emma's mistaken interpretation of Mr Elton's behaviour make you doubt her judgement about Jane and Frank Churchill? Explain.

Past Perfect Continuous

Look at this sentence.

SUBJECT +   HAD BEEN +   ING-FORM OF VERB

He   *had been*   *drinking*   *red wine.*

This sentence is in the **Past Perfect Continuous**. We use this tense to talk about a continuous action that had been happening up to the time that something else happened.

*When we arrived, he **had been reading** for an hour.*

*It **had been snowing** for two hours but then the sun came out.*

Observe the difference between the **Past Continuous** and the **Past Perfect Continuous**.

*I looked out of the window and saw that it **was raining**.*
It was raining in that moment when I looked out the window.

*I looked out of the window and saw that it **had been raining**.*
The ground was wet and there were puddles.
It was not, though, raining in that moment.

3 **Put the verbs in brackets into the *Past Perfect Continuous* or the *Past Continuous* according to the context. There are two examples at the beginning to help you.**

e.g. My brother walked into the living-room. He was covered with dirt from head to toe.
He *(play)* **had been playing** football.

e.g. When I arrived at the field they *(play)* **were playing** football, and they didn't want to stop even though it was raining.

a. I walked into the restaurant and saw some friends of mine. They *(eat)* .... their dinner, but they stopped when they saw me and asked me to join them.

b. I was certain there was something wrong with Julie. Her eyes were red and she kept blowing her nose. She told me that she *(cry)* .... because her best friend was moving to another city.

c. We *(drive)* .... for more than two hours when we finally saw a hotel.

d. I walked into the kitchen but nobody was there. There was flour on the table and the floor. My mother *(bake)* .... a cake for my sister's birthday.

e. When I entered the room I saw Mr Jones. He *(talk)* .... excitedly about Mary. He is generally a very quiet man so I imagine that he *(drink)* .... wine.

f. We looked out of the window on Christmas morning. The sky was blue and the ground white. It *(snow)* ....

g. I saw John at the library last Saturday. He *(look for)* .... books about horses.

h. Philip *(run)* .... along the beach when he heard an explosion.

i. I saw Mike while I *(walk)* .... home. His hair was wet because he *(swim)* ....

j. Alison didn't hear what the teacher said because she *(talk)* .... to her friend.

Read the text about fashion during Jane Austen's lifetime, and think of the word which best fits each space. Use only one word in each space. There is an example at the beginning.

Regency Fashion

Jane Austen was writing (**0**) *during* the period known as the Regency. It was a time (**1**) .... people were very conscious of fashion as (**2**) .... important part of civilized life. Since the eighteenth century, many things (**3**) .... changed. Men (**4**) .... longer wore wigs, but had short haircuts. In *Emma*, when Frank Churchill travels all the way to London (**5**) .... a haircut, Mr Knightley sees it as unsuitable behaviour. Frank Churchill represents the young man of fashion. He buys expensive gloves, he loves social occasions (**6**) .... he sees and is seen. Another change (**7**) .... men's clothing was the wearing of trousers. Previously, 'knee-breeches' had reached only to the knees.

Women's dress changed (**8**) .... The typical woman's dress was very simple, based on ancient Greek dress. A ribbon (**9**) .... tied under the breasts, giving the appearance of a very high waist.

Morning Dress, a plate from *Gallery of Fashion* (1794).

60

Another important **(10)** .... of a woman's outfit was her bonnet, a kind of hat. Bonnets **(11)** .... be very simple or fantastically decorated with flowers and fruit.

Mrs Elton **(12)** .... a large, ridiculous bonnet when she goes strawberry-picking at Donwell Abbey. Generally, **(13)** ...., women's fashions were natural, simple and graceful during the Regency period.

Rooms were light and airy. Furniture was designed to be pleasant and elegant. Different kinds of natural wood were **(14)** .... skilfully to create beautiful pieces of furniture for the houses of the rich. Jane Austen wrote that **(15)** .... of life's greatest pleasures was to 'sit before a fire in a well-proportioned room.'

Morning and Evening Dress from *Le Beau Monde* (1807).

5 **Do the following crossword, at the end you will see the answer to Question 12.**

1. Emma painted Harriet's .... for Mr Elton.
2. Attractive. Nowadays we use this adjective mostly for men, but Jane Austen uses it to describe Emma.
3. To get married you have to find the right ....
4. Isabella is Mr Woodhouse's ....
5. Surprised.
6. Mr Martin, in Emma's opinion, is not particularly attractive or ugly. He is just ....
7. Jane was rather pale, and Emma thought that her .... was not good.
8. In Jane Austen's time, this was an upper-class man with refined manners.
9. A minister of the Anglican Church.
10. Mr Woodhouse gave his daughter everything she wanted, and in this way he .... her.
11. Harriet's parents are dead; she is an ....
12. Mr Knightley believes that Emma has too much of this, and too little understanding.

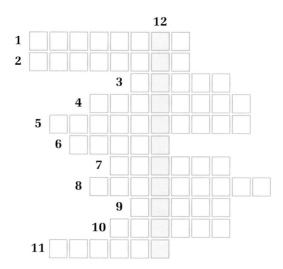

Before you go on

FCE **1** **Listen to the beginning of Part Four, and decide whether the statements are true (T) or false (F).**

	T	F
1. Miss Augusta Hawkins was Mr Elton's fiancée.	☐	☐
2. Harriet visited the Martins for forty minutes.	☐	☐
3. The Martins were very nice to Harriet during her visit.	☐	☐
4. Emma would like Harriet to fall in love with Robert Martin again.	☐	☐
5. Emma is sorry that the Martins belong to a lower social class.	☐	☐
6. Frank Churchill came to visit Emma.	☐	☐
7. He visited the Bates before visiting Emma.	☐	☐
8. Frank has to go to Weymouth to visit Miss Fairfax.	☐	☐

2 **What do you think? Why?**

a. What will the new Mrs Elton be like?

b. Will Harriet fall in love again?

c. Will Jane Fairfax become Emma's friend?

d. Will Mr Knightley and Emma disagree again?

Part Four

A Trifling Young Fellow

M r Elton returned to Highbury with a self-satisfied smile. His fiancée,[2] Miss Augusta Hawkins of Bath and Bristol, was rumoured[3] to be charming, beautiful and perhaps more importantly, in possession of[4] ten thousand pounds a year. He had caught both wealth and affection, all in a few weeks in Bath.

Emma decided that it was best if Harriet visited the Martin family. It would help her forget. But the visit to Abbey Mill Farm only lasted fourteen minutes. Emma did not want Harriet to fall in love again.

---

1. **trifling** : not serious in character.
2. **fiancée** : a woman engaged to be married.
3. **rumoured** : according to gossip, said by people.
4. **in possession of** : having or owning.

A Trifling Young Fellow

'They have been very kind,' Harriet told her.

'It is a pity they do not belong to a higher class,' thought Emma. 'But I cannot allow Harriet to mix with them.'

On the way home, she was pleased to see Mr and Mrs Weston.

'Frank is coming tomorrow,' said Mr Weston excitedly. 'He'll stay for a whole fortnight.' [1]

Next morning, Mr Weston and his son visited Hartfield.

'He is a very good-looking young man,' thought Emma.

'Tell me about life in Highbury, Miss Woodhouse,' Frank asked. 'Do you ride? Are there pleasant walks? Are there balls?'

Emma was aware that Mr Weston was watching her and Frank Churchill together. She knew what he and Mrs Weston hoped for – that Frank and Emma might fall in love and marry. Mr Woodhouse, however, had no such idea.

'Poor young man,' he said. 'Did you have a hard journey? Will you have some gruel, sir, some Hartfield gruel?'

'I must pay one other visit in Highbury,' said Frank. 'At Weymouth, I met a young lady from here, called Miss Fairfax I believe. It would be polite to call on her.'

END

Next day, Emma went out with Mrs Weston to show the village

---

1. **fortnight** : two weeks.

of Highbury to Frank. Seeing the Crown Inn, [1] he immediately said, 'We must organise a ball here.'

'Did you pay your visit yesterday?' she asked.

'Yes, indeed. The aunt talked and talked.'

'What did you think of Miss Fairfax?'

'She looked very pale, almost ill, but very elegant.'

'Did you see her often at Weymouth?'

1. **inn** : a hotel, a large pub with rooms for guests.

Frank had seen the village shop. 'Forgive me, but I must go in and buy some gloves. Then I shall be a true citizen of Highbury.'

Inside the shop, he chose the most fashionable and expensive pair of gloves. 'Yes, I met Miss Fairfax frequently, with the family of Colonel Campbell. The Campbells are very warm-hearted people.' He paused. 'By the way, Miss Woodhouse, have you heard her play the piano?'

'Yes, she plays charmingly.'

'Yes, Mr Dixon, who is an expert in music, always asked her to play.'

Emma smiled. Her imagination had been correct. Jane Fairfax and Mr Dixon were in love!

'Is Mr Dixon very musical [1] then? Miss Fairfax is so reserved that she told us nothing about him.'

'Yes, he loves music. He said no one played as well as Miss Fairfax.'

1. **musical** : fond of music.

'If I had been Miss Campbell,' said Emma, 'I would have been jealous. But Miss Fairfax herself must have been embarrassed by the flattery.' [1]

'I do not know what her feelings were.'

'Of course not. Miss Fairfax is so reserved that her feelings are known only to herself.'

'True. It is impossible to love a reserved person,' agreed Frank Churchill.

The next day, Frank Churchill disappeared from Highbury. He had gone to London to have a haircut. It seemed frivolous [2] to leave his father just to have a fashionable hairstyle. But in all other ways he was an excellent young man. He was open, cheerful, lively, attentive, warm-hearted. Emma was not in love but she would allow others to think that she was.

When Mr Knightley heard about the haircut in London, his face grew dark. 'Hmmm! The young puppy. He is just the trifling [3] silly young fellow I took him for.' [4]

Emma, however, had her own problems. The Coles had invited her to a party. The Coles were a family from a low social class but their business had done well so that now they were rich. Emma, the mistress of Hartfield, was far [5] too snobbish to accept their invitation.

But they had invited all her friends. Frank Churchill would be there. But not Emma. Perhaps there would be dancing.

'What do you think, Mrs Weston,' she asked. 'I cannot accept, can I?'

---

1. **flattery** : high praise from another person.
2. **frivolous** : not sensible, light-hearted.
3. **trifling** : unimportant.
4. **took him for** : imagined him to be.
5. **far** : very much.

'It would be an honour for them if Miss Woodhouse came to their house. Accept their invitation, Emma.'

This was really the advice that Emma wanted to hear. 'Very well, I shall accept. Will there be dancing, do you think?'

In the evening, the carriage took her to the house of the Coles. Mr Knightley arrived at the same time in his own carriage instead of walking as he usually did.

'I am pleased to see you travelling like a gentleman,' she told him.

'Nonsensical ¹ girl!' he replied affectionately.

Frank Churchill seemed to want to spend all his time with her at the party. But there was interesting news.

'A piano has arrived at the home of Miss Bates,' said Mrs Cole. 'It is a very handsome instrument. It is a gift for Miss Fairfax. But no one knows who has sent it!'

'Of course it is from Colonel Campbell.'

'Yes, it must be. But he has not mentioned it in his letters to Jane. It is a great mystery!'

Emma smiled secretively ² at Frank Churchill.

'Do you think it is possible that Mr Dixon has sent the piano? I believe that Mr Dixon and Miss Fairfax were a little in love with each other. Did you know that he saved her from drowning?'

'Yes, I was there. Miss Fairfax nearly fell into the water. Mr Dixon caught her. It all happened in a moment.'

'A moment is enough to fall in love. I am sure that the piano is a gift from Mr Dixon,' she said.

'Yes,' agreed Frank, 'you must be right.'

---

1. **nonsensical** : ridiculous, silly.
2. **secretively** : in a way that hides one's thoughts.

Soon, Harriet and Jane arrived. Emma saw that Frank was staring intently [1] at Jane Fairfax on the other side of the room.

'What is the matter?' she asked.

He woke as if from a dream. 'Excuse me, I am very rude. I was looking at Miss Fairfax's hairstyle. It is very strange. I shall go and ask her about it.'

While Frank went to speak to Jane, Mrs Weston sat with Emma. 'Do you know that Mr Knightley has lent his carriage to Miss Bates and Jane so that they did not have to walk?'

'Indeed,' said Emma. 'Mr Knightley is always very kind and thoughtful.'

'I think it is more than kindness,' whispered Mrs Weston. 'I think he is in love with Jane Fairfax!'

'Mr Knightley and Jane Fairfax!' exclaimed Emma. 'No, Mr Knightley must not marry. Isabella's children would not inherit [2] Donwell Abbey. Poor little Henry. And Jane Fairfax, of all women!'

'Jane has always been his favourite, as you know.'

'Please, Mrs Weston, do not become a match-maker. Jane Fairfax cannot be mistress of Donwell Abbey.'

'Perhaps he has sent her the piano.'

'Mr Knightley does nothing mysteriously. I do not believe that he has any idea of marrying Jane Fairfax.'

'Well, Frank wants you to sing with him. Go to him, Emma.'

After Emma and Frank had sung at the piano, Frank sang with

---

1. **intently** : with great concentration.
2. **inherit** : receive property from someone after his/her death.

Jane Fairfax. She played with great talent. Mr Knightley sat watching them with Emma.

'The piano is a very kind gift from the Campbells,' she said, testing him.

'Yes, but they should have warned her that it was coming. Surprises are foolish things.' He paused, looking angrily towards the piano. 'Frank Churchill is asking her to sing another song. She is already tired. He only thinks about his own pleasure. He is a trifling silly young fellow.'

He spoke to Miss Bates and she rescued Jane.

Dancing followed. Emma and Frank Churchill led the dance. She looked to see if Mr Knightley danced with Jane but he was talking to Mrs Cole.

'You dance beautifully, Miss Woodhouse,' said Frank Churchill as he helped her into her carriage at the end of the party.

Go back to the text

1 **Answer the following questions.**

a. What is the first thing Frank thinks of when he sees the Crown Inn?
....

b. How does Frank become a true citizen of Highbury?
....

c. Why does Emma conclude that Mr Dixon must be in love with Jane Fairfax?
....

d. Why did Frank Churchill go to London?
....

e. What do people think of his reason for going to London?
....

f. Why was Emma undecided about going to the Coles' party?
....

g. What was the interesting news at the party?
....

h. Why was Frank staring at Jane?
....

i. According to Emma, why shouldn't Mr Knightley marry Jane?
....

j. What does Mr Knightley think of Frank Churchill?
....

2 **What do you think? Why?**

a. Is Emma's imagination usually correct?

b. Who is right about Frank's character?

c. Does Emma think too much about romance?

d. Would Harriet be happier if she had never met Emma?

Third conditional

Look at these examples of the third conditional. We use it when we imagine what would have happened if the past had been different. But it is too late to change things!

If Emma **hadn't influenced** Harriet, she **might have married** Mr Martin.
Miss Taylor **would have stayed** at Hartfield **if** she **hadn't got** married.

The sentences follow this structure:

If	+	PAST PERFECT,	+	CONDITIONAL PERFECT
		had + past participle		**would**
				might + **have** + **past participle**
				could

3 Match the elements in column A with the elements in column B to form third conditional sentences that make sense within the context of the story. You must decide which elements form the if-clause of each sentence. There is an example at the beginning.

0. [d] If Harriet hadn't had a sore throat, she would have gone to the party.

A

0. [d] Harriet/go/to the party

1. [ ] Mr Elton/propose

2. [ ] Emma/have/more understanding than imagination

3. [ ] Mr Woodhouse/be/happier

4. [ ] Jane/drown

5. [ ] Emma/accept/Mr Elton's marriage proposal

6. [ ] He/come to Highbury/more often

B

a. Mr Dixon/not save/Jane

b. Mr Weston's first wife/not die

c. His aunt/let him

d. Harriet/have/a sore throat

e. He/not marry/ Augusta Hawkins

f. John Knightley/get in/ the right carriage

g. Emma/guess that Mr Elton was in love with her

Writing

 4 **Pretend you are a newspaper reporter who has attended the Coles' party. Write in 120-180 words a description of the party saying who were there and what they talked about.**
Include the following information:

− Frank Churchill, and what kind of person he is

− What Emma was doing

− The big news of the party and the various explanations you heard

− What you think of the people you met

You can begin like this:

Highbury Society News

The Mysterious Gift

Last night your Highbury high-society reporter attended the lovely party thrown by the Cole family. As my readers will surely remember, the Coles were once poor but now they are ....

....

....

....

....

....

....

....

....

....

These then were the words and ways of Highbury's finest.

Characters

5 Frank Churchill is a very pleasant young man. Emma thinks that he
is intelligent, good-looking and lively. Mr Knightley, however,
thinks that he is spoilt and irresponsible. He has been brought up by
a rich family and has an easy, luxurious, expensive life. He only
thinks about haircuts, dances and romance. Who is right?

It is often possible to have two different opinions about the same
person. Here are some names of famous people. Choose two
adjectives to describe each person. Then show your list to a friend.
Do they agree?

Princess Diana	President John Kennedy
Gandhi	Marie Curie
Napoleon	Marilyn Monroe
Shakespeare	Hitler
Jane Austen	Martin Luther King
Cleopatra	The President of your country
Garibaldi	Bill Gates

Here is a list of possible adjectives. Use others if you wish:

ambitious	attractive	boring	cunning
dishonest	evil	fascinating	good-hearted
hard-working	imaginative	intelligent	inventive
lively	mad	passionate	powerful
selfish	successful	unselfish	wise

6 What do you think? Why?

   a. Is there a 'perfect' character?

   b. Is it wrong to live a luxurious lifestyle?

   c. Is it easy to know if someone is sincere?

   d. Do you prefer serious people or frivolous people?

   e. What are the most important qualities in a friend?

Speaking

T: GRADE 8

7 Theme – Hypothetical Situations
Look at the pictures on pages 65 and 71. If you had been Frank
Churchill or Emma what would you have liked about your lifestyle?

Include some of the following aspects:

   – clothes

   – hobbies

   – friends

   – money

   – social status

Leisure in Early Nineteenth-Century England

Emma gives us some indication of how the English upper classes enjoyed themselves at this time. There were many fashionable resorts [1] with a lively social life in Jane Austen's England. Mr Elton goes to Bath for a long stay. In Bath we hear that he attends dances and other social gatherings. [2] It seems possible for him to leave his duties as vicar of Highbury without any problem. Frank Churchill

A general view of Bath from the Claverton Road (1806),
by John Claude Nattes.

1. **resorts** : holiday towns.
2. **gatherings** : meetings of people.

and Jane Fairfax both go on holiday to Weymouth where Jane has a near-accident at a 'water-party', an excursion by boat. The Churchills come to London from Yorkshire in order to enjoy the social opportunities of the capital. John Knightley and his family go to Southend on the coast. At one point, everyone is looking at pictures of Switzerland, reminding us that foreign travel was also popular among the rich.

Bath had been established for a long time as a fashionable resort for the upper classes. They went there to 'take the waters', natural spring water which had been known since Roman times. The city had been re-built and re-designed in the eighteenth century in the latest style of elegant neo-classical [1] architecture. It remains one of the most beautiful cities in England although Jane Austen herself did not enjoy living there.

Weymouth was a fashionable resort in the Regency period.

1. **neo-classical** : of a style of art that is based on or influenced by the classical style.

The seaside towns were gaining popularity. Along the south and south-east coast, which had the best climate, seaside resorts developed. Jane Austen visited places like Teignmouth in Devon and Lyme Regis for pleasure. One of her minor novels, *Sanditon*, describes a 'young and rising bathing place'. Emma, however, had never seen the sea. Mr Woodhouse would have been too worried! In fact, sea-bathing was considered good for the health. You couldn't just jump in the sea, however. Men and women were strictly separated on different areas of the beach. Nobody was allowed to see you in your bathing costume even though these covered the whole body. The bathers reached the sea in 'bathing machines', horse-drawn [1] carriages which went out into the water. Women known as 'dippers' were waiting to help the bathers into the sea. It was a very complicated business!

A view of Lyme Regis (1810).

1. **horse-drawn** : pulled by horse.

1 Answer the following questions.

a. Name some of the places where the upper-class English went for holidays during the nineteenth century.

....

b. What were 'water-parties'?

....

c. What does 'take the waters' mean?

....

d. In what architectural style is Bath?

....

e. Which type of holiday spot was becoming popular in Jane Austen's day?

....

f. What was one of the reasons why people went 'sea-bathing'?

....

g. How were the beaches separated?

....

h. What were 'bathing machines' and why did people use them?

....

i. Who were 'dippers'?

....

Part Five

In Love or not in Love?

*E*mma looked back on the party with great pleasure. The Coles would always remember the visit of Miss Woodhouse, the mistress of Hartfield. But she wished she could play the piano and sing as well as Jane. She now sat down to practise. But Harriet interrupted her.

'I wish I could play like you, Miss Woodhouse. Everybody said how well you played.'

'The truth is that Jane Fairfax has far more talent and skill.'

'Mr Frank Churchill said that you had more taste.'

Emma and Harriet went to the village where they met Mrs Weston and Frank.

'We are going to call on Miss Bates. Frank tells me that I promised to visit them to hear the new piano. I don't remember making such a promise, but Frank insists it is true. Join us after your shopping.'

Miss Bates came to fetch Emma and Harriet from the shop.

'Mr Knightley is so kind to Jane. Jane told him how much she enjoyed eating apples and, the same evening, he sent a servant with a year's supply of apples. They are the best...'

She talked and talked. 'So Mr Knightley has given Jane Fairfax the Donwell Abbey apples,' Emma was thinking confusedly, remembering Mrs Weston's idea.

Frank Churchill smiled warmly when he saw Emma. Jane was at the new piano, preparing to play. Frank begged her to play a waltz from Weymouth. 'It's good to hear music which has made one happy.'

At that moment, Miss Bates saw Mr Knightley riding by outside the house.

She called to him from the window. 'Mr Knightley, will you join us? Miss Woodhouse and Miss Smith are here.'

'Well, perhaps for five minutes.'

'And Mr Frank Churchill is here.'

Hearing his name, Mr Knightley changed his mind. 'No, I have no time. Your room is full enough.'

'Thank you for the apples. Ah, he has gone.'

Meanwhile, Frank Churchill and Emma had begun planning a ball. It may be possible for young people to live without dancing. But when a beginning is made, they always want more.

'We shall hold the ball at the Crown Inn,' said Frank Churchill. 'May I hope for the honour of your hand for the first two dances, Miss Woodhouse?'

She heard Mr Weston whispering to his wife. 'He has asked her to dance with him. I knew he would!'

Even Jane Fairfax looked forward to the ball with great pleasure. Only Mr Knightley was indifferent [1] to the idea.

'I will be there,' he said, 'but I do not enjoy watching others dance.'

Two days later, however, a letter arrived from Yorkshire. Frank's aunt, Mrs Churchill, was seriously ill. He must return immediately and the ball must be cancelled. Emma was wretchedly [2] disappointed.

Frank Churchill came to Hartfield before he left.

'I hate saying goodbye,' he said. 'I am very uncertain when I can return. If my uncle and aunt come to London this spring... But I am afraid my aunt will be too unwell. If I come again, we shall have our ball. Do not forget your promise to dance with me.'

Emma smiled graciously. [3] 'Have you said goodbye to Miss Bates and Miss Fairfax?' she asked.

'Yes, I have called there...' He hesitated, got up and walked to the window. 'Perhaps, Miss Woodhouse, you already suspect...'

He looked at her as if he was trying to read her thoughts. She did not know what to say. Was he preparing to declare his love

---

1. **indifferent** : having no interest in something.

2. **wretchedly** : miserably, very badly.

3. **graciously** : kindly, generously.

for her? He said nothing but sighed. He was more in love with her than she had supposed.

Then Mr Weston entered. Soon, father and son had gone. 'He seems to love me,' thought Emma. 'And I think that I am a little in love with him.'

After Frank had left, however, Emma wondered if she was really in love. Or was it just imagination? She was not unhappy without him. She imagined Frank Churchill proposing [1] to her. She invented [2] interesting conversations, elegant letters, amusing schemes to bring them together. But, in her imagination, she always ended by refusing him.

'I am glad that he is not necessary to my happiness. I am quite enough in love,' she thought. 'He does not have a very steady character and he will soon love somebody else. They say everybody is in love once in their lives. If this is my one time, then I have escaped very easily.'

At this time, Mr Elton was bringing his new bride, Mrs Augusta Elton, back to Highbury. 'Be calm, Harriet,' said Emma.

'Oh, Miss Woodhouse, you have been my best friend.'

'Yes,' thought Emma, 'Harriet will make a sweet, obedient, [3] lovely wife. Perhaps even for Frank Churchill.'

Emma and Harriet visited the newly-married couple. Mr Elton was embarrassed. Even Emma felt sorry for him. How unlucky for him to be in the same room with the woman he had just got married to, the woman he had wanted to marry and the woman he had been expected to marry.

'His wife is charming,' said Harriet afterwards.

Emma, however, did not agree. When Mrs Elton visited

1. **proposing** : asking somebody to marry you.
2. **invented** : thought of things that did not exist.
3. **obedient** : doing what you are told to do.

Hartfield, she became convinced [1] that she was a vain, self-satisfied, self-important, ignorant [2] woman. She immediately began talking about her rich brother-in-law.

'Hartfield is very like Maple Grove, where my sister Selina lives. I have spent many happy months there. My brother and sister will visit us in the summer in their barouche-landau. [3] Last summer, we went everywhere in their barouche-landau. Selina loves going for a drive with me in her barouche-landau. Do you and Mr Woodhouse have a barouche-landau, Miss Woodhouse?'

'No, Mrs Elton,' said Emma coldly.

'You must come to Bath. Your father can take the waters [4] for his health and I can introduce you to the best society.'

'What a rude, ill-mannered woman,' Emma was thinking.

'I have just met Knightley,' continued Mrs Elton. 'As you know, he is the best friend of my caro sposo. [5] Knightley is quite the gentleman. I like him.'

At last they were gone. Emma could breathe.

'What a terrible woman. She called Mr Knightley 'Knightley'! She has discovered that he is a gentleman. I do not think that he will discover that she is a lady!'

'Well, my dear,' said Mr Woodhouse, 'she seems a very pretty young lady. She speaks a little quickly. Her voice rather hurts the ear. It is better not to marry.'

When Mrs Elton realised that Emma did not like her, she became cold and distant towards her. But, worse, she was

1. **convinced** : firm in someone's belief.
2. **ignorant** : knowing little or nothing.
3. **barouche-landau** : a very fashionable kind of carriage; Mrs Elton is proud of it, so mentions it several times.
4. **take the waters** : from Roman times, the city of Bath was famous for its spa waters.
5. **caro sposo** : 'dear husband'; Mrs Elton wants to be fashionable.

sarcastic [1] towards Harriet. Instead, Mrs Elton decided to make Jane Fairfax her special friend. 'Jane is absolutely charming, Miss Woodhouse,' she said when they met. 'We must help her in every way that we can.'

'Miss Fairfax should not have to put up with [2] Mrs Elton,' said Mr Knightley.

Emma was surprised by the passion with which he spoke. Was Mrs Weston right? Did he love Jane Fairfax?

Mr Knightley continued talking about Jane Fairfax, praising her good qualities.

'You certainly think very highly of Jane,' said Emma.

'Yes, it is no secret,' he replied.

'And yet...' She hesitated, then hurried on. 'The size of your admiration for her may take you by surprise [3] one day.'

'I know what you are thinking, Emma. Others think so. But you are mistaken. I am sure Miss Fairfax would not have me if I asked her and I am very sure I shall never ask her. I see you have been match-making in your imagination again.'

'No, I have not. I have not the smallest wish that you should marry Jane Fairfax or Jane Anybody.'

'No, Emma, I do not think I will ever be in love with Jane Fairfax. She is a charming young woman – but not even Jane Fairfax is perfect. She has a fault. She hasn't got the open character which a man would wish for in a wife.'

'Well, Mrs Weston,' Emma said after he had left, 'what do you think now?'

'Why, he is so sure that he is not in love with her that he may in the end find the opposite is true!'

1. **sarcastic** : making bitter remarks intended to hurt someone's feelings.
2. **put up with** : bear.
3. **take you by surprise** : attack you unexpectedly or without warning.

Go back to the text

FCE **1** **Choose the correct answer (A, B, C or D) for each question.**

1. How does Frank Churchill compliment Emma's piano playing?
   A ☐ He says she plays better than Jane.
   B ☐ He says her playing is elegant.
   C ☐ He says she has more taste than Jane.
   D ☐ He says she knows more songs.

2. Why is Emma confused when she hears that Mr Knightley sent Jane apples?
   A ☐ Because she is convinced that he does not love Jane, but this action may mean that he does.
   B ☐ Because Mr Knightley does not usually do such nice things.
   C ☐ Because this is a mysterious action, and she is convinced that Mr Knightley never does anything mysterious.
   D ☐ Because Mrs Weston had told her that Mr Knightley was in love with Jane and his attention to her seems to offer proof.

3. Why does Mr Knightley refuse Miss Bates's invitation to come in?
   A ☐ Because she tells him that Emma is there.
   B ☐ Because she tells him that Jane is there.
   C ☐ Because he does not like music.
   D ☐ Because she tells him that Frank is there.

4. Why does Emma begin to think that Frank Churchill is very much in love with her?
   A ☐ Because he came to say goodbye to her.
   B ☐ Because he asked her to dance at the ball.
   C ☐ Because he was about to reveal something personal to her when he was interrupted.
   D ☐ Because he only seems interested in her.

5. According to Mr Knightley, why will he never marry Jane Fairfax?
   A ☐ Because she will not marry him, and he will not ask her.
   B ☐ Because she is really in love with Frank Churchill.
   C ☐ Because she is in love with Mr Dixon.
   D ☐ Because he wants to marry someone else.

2 **What do you think? Why?**

a. For what reasons does Emma dislike Mrs Elton?

b. Do you think there may be another reason why Mr Knightley doesn't like Frank other than him being rather silly?

c. Do you believe that Mr Knightley is in love with Jane Fairfax?

Vocabulary

3 **Underline the complete phrasal verb in each sentence, and then choose the verb in the box that has the same meaning.**

> raise   be tired of   postpone   tolerate   end
> act in a way to attract the attention of others

a. Mr Knightley does not think that Jane should have to put up with Mrs Elton.

b. Frank Churchill had to put off his visit to Highbury.

c. Emma wanted Harriet to break off her relationship with the Martins.

d. I am fed up with listening to Miss Bates.

e. Jane had been brought up by the Campbells.

f. Mrs Elton loves to show off.

Now fill in the gaps with phrasal verbs from the sentences above.

a. Her parents did not .... Sally up very well. In fact, she is rather spoilt.

b. Herbert played the piano and sang because he wanted to .... in front of his new girlfriend. Unfortunately, he later discovered that she hates music.

c. It is raining, so I am afraid we will have to .... our tennis match until next week.

d. I do not understand why I have to .... this noise. I am going to tell my neighbours to lower the music.

e. My mother is .... us making a mess in the kitchen.

f. Susan has .... her engagement with Jack. She has decided to marry another man.

Looking at the text

4 **Go back to page 84 and read the text from 'Emma and Harriet visited...' to page 85 'Knightley is quite the gentleman'.**

a. Why was Mr Elton embarrassed?

b. Imagine you were a fly on the wall. Describe what each person was wearing, doing, feeling and saying.

c. What are the six adjectives which Emma uses to describe Mrs Elton during this part of the story?

d. For the above adjectives find words or prefixes which mean the opposite. Now use any of the twelve adjectives to describe someone you know.

e. What language do you think the word 'barouche-landau' comes from. Use a good dictionary to find out.

f. How many times does Mrs Elton refer to the 'barouche-landau'? Why?

g. What are the two main reasons why the Woodhouses should come to Bath, in Mrs Elton's opinion?

Characters

5 **Mrs Elton is a vulgar snob. She is one of the strongest characters in the book. She has a very loud voice, she boasts about her rich relatives and she loves to control other people. Most readers think that she is very unpleasant. But she shares a lot of qualities with Emma. They are both snobbish, they both like to be the centre of attention and they both try to help a less fortunate friend. Write a monologue by a modern Mrs Elton. Here are some ideas she boasts about:**

her:

sister's private jet
house in Florida
rich husband in the computer industry
plans for the future
world trip
Paris and Milan-designed clothes
friendship with royalty

You can begin:

'My sister is coming to fetch me next week. We're flying in her private jet to the States...'

Notice that you can use the Present Continuous tense to describe plans in the future.

 Read the text below and look carefully at each line. Some of the lines are correct and some have a word which should not be there. If a line is correct, put a tick (✓) by the number below. If a line has a word which should not be there, write the word by the number. There are two examples at the beginning.

Leisure

Brighton on the south coast was the most very	**0.** *very*
famous seaside resort. The Prince of Wales loved it	**00.** ✓
and had the Royal Pavilion built there. The	**1.** ....
Brighton Pavilion was been designed in	**2.** ....
fashionable Indian and Chinese styles; this showed	**3.** ....
off the influence of Britain's expanding empire.	**4.** ....
During the Napoleonic wars, large numbers of the	**5.** ....
soldiers were stationed there to defend off the coast	**6.** ....
against a possible attack from France. This gave	**7.** ....
Brighton the reputation as a dangerous place for	**8.** ....
love affairs and adventure.	**9.** ....
In Jane Austen's novel *Pride and Prejudice*, one of	**10.** ....
the heroine's sisters runs away with a soldier to	**11.** ....
Brighton. Like Bath and Weymouth, Brighton was	**12.** ....
associated with scandal. More peaceful leisure	**13.** ....
activities are also mentioned about in *Emma*. There	**14.** ....
is the ball at the Cross Inn, the excursion to Box	**15.** ....

A drawing of Harleston Park in Northamptonshire (1820),
by Humphrey Repton.

Hill, the Donwell strawberry party and a series of dinners and musical evenings. Harriet and her friend go for a walk along in the countryside. Jane doesn't plays the piano. Emma paints.

Country houses such as Hartfield and Donwell Abbey were partly designed for pleasure. There were beautiful gardens, often with a lake or wood.

16. ....
17. ....
18. ....
19. ....
20. ....
21. ....
22. ....

Before you go on

FCE **1** Listen to the beginning of Part Six, and complete the missing information in the sentences below. You will need a word or a short phrase.

1. Emma decided to invite the Eltons because she did not want people to think that ....

2. Jane says that she always walks to the post office because it ....

3. Mr Woodhouse thinks that young ladies are ....

4. Mrs Elton thinks that Jane should find a job as ....
   ....

5. Jane does not wish to find a job until ....

6. Frank would be able to visit Highbury often during the summer because his aunt had recovered and ....

7. Mr Weston hopes that Mrs Elton will ....

8. Mrs Elton think that nobodies often ....

9. As soon as the carriage with Miss Bates and Jane arrived, Frank ....

10. When Miss Bates entered she ....

2 Answer the following questions.

a. Will Frank Churchill return to Highbury?

b. Will Emma find out Jane's secret?

c. Will Mr Knightley get married?

d. Will Mrs Elton gain her revenge on Emma and Harriet?

Part Six

Harriet is Rescued Twice!

verybody in Highbury invited the newly-married couple to dinner. 'We are quite the fashion,' said Mrs Elton proudly.

'I must invite them also,' thought Emma, 'or people will accuse me of being jealous.'

'I saw you walking in the rain this morning, Miss Fairfax,' said John Knightley at the dinner. He was visiting from London. 'I hope you did not have to go far.'

'I went only to the post office. I always fetch the letters when I am here. A walk before breakfast does me good.'

Mr Woodhouse had been listening. 'Young ladies must take care of themselves in bad weather. They are delicate plants. Did you change your stockings, my dear?'

Mrs Elton now added her opinion. 'You must not go for your letters in the rain, Miss Fairfax. I shall speak to Mr E. One of our servants will fetch them for you.'

'Excuse me,' said Jane seriously, 'but I cannot consent. [1] It is a pleasure for me to go to the post office. That is the end of the matter.'

Emma was wondering, 'Do Jane Fairfax's letters come from Ireland? From Mr Dixon?'

'You must soon find a job as a governess, Jane,' said Mrs Elton. 'I am sure my sister at Maple Grove can find you a suitable position with an excellent family.'

'I shall see the Campbells in London in the summer. I do not wish to find a job until then.'

'But my dear child, it is already April. I shall ask my sister to start looking.'

'No,' repeated Jane. 'I wish to stay as I am for three or four months.'

Mr Weston arrived late at the party with a letter in his hands. 'Read it,' he said. 'Only a few lines. Read it to Emma.'

The letter was from Frank Churchill. His aunt had recovered and decided to come to London. Frank would be able to visit Highbury frequently during the summer. Emma felt strangely excited but also worried.

'I hope I shall soon have the pleasure of introducing my son to you,' Mr Weston said to Mrs Elton.

'I and my caro sposo will look forward to [2] meeting him. He lives with a great family, I believe. Does Mrs Churchill have a barouche-landau?'

1. **consent** : agree.
2. **look forward to** : wait with pleasure for something to happen.

Harriet is Rescued Twice!

'Mrs Churchill is an arrogant, [1] insolent [2] woman. I should not speak badly of her but she keeps Frank away from me. She was a nobody [3] until she married Mr Churchill.'

'A nobody! They often make the most noise,' said Mrs Elton.

When Frank Churchill visited Highbury again, he seemed happy but less in love with Emma. One thing was sure. The ball at the Crown Inn would take place after all.

The day of the ball arrived. Frank was nervous. He seemed to be waiting for somebody to arrive.

Soon, the Eltons came. 'My caro sposo and I will send our carriage for Miss Bates and Jane,' said Mrs Elton loudly. As soon as the carriage arrived, Frank went out with umbrellas to protect them from the rain.

'He is a very fine young man, Mr Weston,' said Mrs Elton.

Miss Bates entered, talking continuously. 'No rain at all... And Jane says... Well, this is brilliant. So well lighted. Oh, Mr Weston. Oh, Mr Elton...' She did not stop talking for the next ten minutes. END

The dancing was ready to begin.

'I am sorry, Emma,' said Mrs Weston, 'but Mrs Elton must lead the dance. We must honour the new wife.'

Emma was disappointed but accepted the situation calmly. She and Frank Churchill stood second to Mrs Elton and Mr Weston. It was almost enough to make her think of marrying. However, she greatly enjoyed the evening. She felt sad though that Mr Knightley was not dancing. He stood with the older men, often watching Emma as she danced with Frank Churchill. She noticed how he stood out [4] from all the other men with his tall figure, broad shoulders and gentlemanly manners.

1. **arrogant** : showing too much pride in oneself and too little consideration for others.
2. **insolent** : very rude.
3. **nobody** : unimportant person.
4. **stood out** : was easily seen or noticed.

The partners changed, then changed again. Emma noticed that Harriet had no partner. Mr Elton was the only gentleman free but, although he deliberately passed near Harriet, he did not ask her to dance.

'Do you not dance, Mr Elton?' Mrs Weston asked him.

'Most readily [1] with you, madam,' he said gallantly.

'I am no dancer. You must get a better partner.'

'I will dance with Mrs Gilbert.'

'No, I would like to see Miss Smith dancing.'

Mr Elton smiled cruelly. 'Miss Smith! You must excuse me. I am an old married man, my dancing days are over.' He then joined Mr Knightley's group, exchanging another cruel smile with his wife. Poor Harriet sat alone.

Then Emma saw a wonderful thing. Mr Knightley led Harriet to the dance. Emma had never felt more surprised or more delighted. He was a very good dancer and Harriet herself was full of lovely smiles.

Mr Elton left the room.

'Knightley has taken pity on [2] poor Miss Smith,' said Mrs Elton loudly. 'It is very good-natured [3] of him.'

Emma searched for Mr Knightley with her eyes. He came to her side and she thanked him.

'Mr Elton was unpardonably [4] rude. And Mrs Elton's looks were also inexcusable,' [5] he said. 'They aimed at wounding [6] more than Harriet. Emma, why are they your enemies?'

1. **readily** : willingly, eagerly.
2. **taken pity on** : felt sorry for.
3. **good-natured** : kind, generous.
4. **unpardonably** : very, extremely.
5. **inexcusable** : that cannot be forgiven.
6. **wounding** : hurting deliberately.

She did not reply.

'You did want him to marry Harriet. Confess it, Emma.'

'I did,' replied Emma, 'and they cannot forgive me. I admit that I was completely mistaken in Mr Elton. There is a littleness [1] about him which you discovered and I did not.'

'You would have chosen for him better than he chose himself. Harriet is a modest, natural girl that any man of sense [2] and taste would prefer to Mrs Elton.'

Emma was very pleased.

'Who are you going to dance with?' asked Mr Knightley.

Emma hesitated a moment and then replied, 'With you, if you will ask me.'

'Will you?' he said, offering his hand.

'Of course. You have shown me you can dance and we are not so much brother and sister that it is improper.' [3]

'Brother and sister? Certainly not!'

Next day, Emma sat remembering the ball and Mr Knightley's kindness to her friend. 'Perhaps my life is really perfect,' she thought. Just then, the great gates of Hartfield swung [4] open. Two people entered – Frank Churchill with Harriet, white and frightened, leaning on his arm.

As soon as they were in the hall, Harriet fainted. [5] Recovering, she told Emma her story.

She and another girl had gone for a walk in the country along the London road. Some distance beyond Highbury, as the road

1. **littleness** : unkindness.
2. **man of sense** : intelligent man.
3. **improper** : socially incorrect, wrong.
4. **swung** : moved in a curve.
5. **fainted** : lost consciousness.

turned suddenly, covered by trees on either side, they saw a group of gipsies [1] ahead of them at the edge of the forest. A gipsy child came towards them to beg. [2] Harriet's friend was frightened. She screamed, climbed up a steep [3] bank and ran back towards the village. But poor Harriet could not follow. Her legs were tired after dancing.

The gipsy children, led by a strong woman and a great boy, surrounded her. More and more frightened, she took out her purse and gave them a shilling. [4] She begged them to let her go and was slowly moving away. But her terror and her purse had excited them and the whole gang followed her, demanding more.

Fortunately, Frank Churchill was walking along the same road. 'It was lucky,' he explained. 'I went to the house of Miss Bates to return some borrowed scissors before I left. I was walking along the road to find my servant and the horses.'

As soon as they saw him, the gipsies ran away. Frank immediately brought Harriet to Hartfield. That was the whole story.

Emma's imagination was on fire. [5] A fine young man and a lovely young woman had shared a great adventure. Of course, they must fall in love as a result. It was certain!

Next day, Harriet burnt everything that she had kept in

---

1. **gipsies** : travelling people.
2. **beg** : ask for money.
3. **steep** : at a sharp angle, difficult to climb.
4. **shilling** : a small coin (no longer used in England).
5. **on fire** : excited.

memory of her love for Mr Elton – a pencil he had used, a plaster [1] he had given her. 'My heart is given to a man who is very superior to Mr Elton,' she told Emma seriously.

Emma smiled. She was sure that Harriet was referring to Frank Churchill. 'I am not surprised. He rendered [2] you a great service.'

'Yes, he rescued my heart,' sighed Harriet.

That evening everyone was together at Hartfield. Mr Knightley was worried. A strange thing had happened. Frank Churchill had asked Mrs Weston if Mr Perry, the village chemist, had bought a carriage yet. 'You wrote to me in a letter three months ago that he planned to do so.'

'Impossible! I have never heard of any such plan.'

'I must have dreamed it,' said Frank.

'It was a strange dream,' interrupted Miss Bates. 'Mr Perry told me about three months ago that he wanted to buy a carriage. But I told nobody except Jane. Then he changed his mind. Your dream was true, Mr Churchill.'

Mr Knightley saw that Frank was confused and that Jane hid her face.

After tea, Emma and her visitors played a game. Each person was given some letters which they had to

---

1. **plaster** : something to cover a small cut or wound.
2. **rendered** : gave.

rearrange into a word. During the game, Frank Churchill handed some letters to Jane Fairfax. She smiled and pushed the letters away. At once, Harriet innocently [1] took them and, sitting next to Mr Knightley, turned to him for help. The word was B-L-U-N-D-E-R. [2]

Mr Knightley continued to watch. Frank and Emma were laughing together. Then Frank took more letters to Jane. X, D, N, O, I. The word was DIXON. Jane looked up, blushed deeply and angrily mixed the letters again. Then she turned to her aunt and said that she wished to go home.

'Emma,' said Mr Knightley later, 'have you ever thought that there is an attachment [3] between Frank Churchill and Jane Fairfax?'

'Never! Never! What ridiculous [4] ideas you have!'

1. **innocently** : with little or no knowledge about something.
2. **blunder** : a serious mistake.
3. **attachment** : a romantic relationship.
4. **ridiculous** : silly.

Go back to the text

FCE **1** **Answer the following questions. Choose from the characters (A-E). There is an example at the beginning.**

A Emma   B Jane   C Frank
D Mr Knightley   E Harriet

Who:

0. [B] walks to fetch his/her letters?

1. [ ] refuses Mrs Elton's offers of help?

2. [ ] stood and watched Emma dancing with Frank?

3. [ ] did Mr Elton treat badly at the dance?

4. [ ] thinks that the Eltons wanted to hurt Emma's feelings?

5. [ ] compliments Emma's match-making skills?

6. [ ] saved Harriet from the gipsies?

7. [ ] made a great blunder?

8. [ ] knew about the chemist's interest in a carriage besides Miss Bates and Frank?

9. [ ] believes that Frank and Jane are in love?

2 **If Jane and Frank are actually in love as Mr Knightley thinks, what then would be the explanation for the following facts?**

a. Jane's insisting on going to fetch her own letters.

b. Frank's knowledge of the chemist's interest in a carriage.

c. Jane's refusal to compose the word 'BLUNDER' with her letters.

d. Jane's embarrassed and angry reaction to the word 'DIXON'.

Joining sentences

3 We can use words like:

> after   although   and   as   because
> before   if   since   so   when   while

to join sentences. Look at the story below. In each numbered space, put a suitable word from the list above.

THE GIPSIES' STORY

1.................... we were camping at the side of the road, we saw two young ladies walking towards us. We thought that they were lost, 2.................... we decided to help them. However, 3.................... we approached them, one of the girls ran away. The other one didn't move, perhaps 4.................... she was so frightened. She offered us money 5.................... we hadn't asked for anything. 6.................... we were trying to comfort her, a young man appeared. 7.................... we had time to explain, he took out a stick 8.................... began beating us. It was very unfair. 9.................... he and the girl had gone away, we left the area. 10.................... the police find us, they will put us in prison 11.................... nobody believes a gipsy.

Vocabulary

4 Match the words in column A with their opposites in column B. There are three extra words in column A; with these three words form their opposites by either adding prefixes or by changing the suffixes. Write these in the spaces at the bottom of column B.

	A		B
wealth	•	•	cruel
affection	•	•	open
kind	•	•	serious
expensive	•	•	inferior
good-looking	•	•	kindly
polite	•	•	reject
fashionable	•	•	rude
reserved	•	•	poverty
frivolous	•	•	dislike
handsome	•	•	ugly
thoughtful	•	•	bad-natured
warmly	•	•	unattractive
uncertain	•	•	certain
mistaken	•	•	coldly
accept	•	•	right
cruelly	•	•	
good-natured	•	•	
superior	•	•	

Writing

 5 Harriet Smith and Jane Fairfax are both orphans. In other ways they are very different. Harriet is sweet, shy and modest without any special talents. She is warm-hearted, loving and unreserved. She tells Emma all her dreams and accepts her advice. Jane, on the other hand, is talented, elegant but rather cold and secretive. She seems to feel things deeply.

Answer one of the following questions (A or B).

A   Write a letter to either Harriet or Jane in which you give them advice. Write your letter in 120-180 words.

In your letter to Harriet say whether:
– she should listen to Emma;
– she should think so much about love;
– what the best thing for her to do is.

In your letter to Jane Fairfax say whether:
– she should tell her secrets to a friend;
– she should accept a job;
– she should earn her living as a pianist.

B   Upper-class women in Jane Austen's time without a husband were in a difficult position, and if they were orphans their situation was even worse. Write a short report on the situation of unwed women without families as it is shown in *Emma*. Write your report in 120-180 words. You can use the following information:

– the only ladylike work available, such as sewing and teaching, was poorly paid;

– an upper-class lady could be a governess, but it was a lonely job – a governess was neither a normal servant nor a member of the family;

– upper-class women were almost completely dependent on men for survival – a good marriage was, therefore, a question of survival;

– estates could only be inherited by males and only widowed women could possess property.

Read the text below and decide which answer (A, B, C or D) best fits each space. There is an example at the beginning.

At Home and Abroad

(0) _D_ we read *Emma*, it is easy to forget that it was written at a time of European war. Jane Fairfax's father was killed while serving overseas. (1) .... is the only small detail which reminds us that England had (2) .... war on France in 1793, and had then become heavily involved in the wars against Napoleon. Nelson, the British admiral (3) .... statue stands in Trafalgar Square in the centre of London, and Wellington, the general at the battle of Waterloo, were national heroes.

Two of Jane Austen's brothers were in the British navy and she took a keen interest in the developments of the war. In her last major novel, *Persuasion*, she introduces naval officers (4) .... important characters. In *Emma*, however, her interest was in the life of the ladies and gentlemen of the English countryside, (5) .... away from the wars.

There is also no (6) .... of British politics. There were two main parties, the Whigs, the more liberal party, and the Tories, who were conservative. George III was King of England, but while he suffered from a form of madness his son was Prince Regent, who later became George IV. (7) .... she dedicated *Emma* to him, Jane Austen did not approve of the Prince Regent. He had a reputation (8) .... immorality. He loved Mrs Fitzherbert, but had married Princess Caroline. Jane Austen wrote that she supported Caroline 'because she was a woman'. Many events (9) .... place which suggested how the future would develop. The slave trade was (10) .... The first steam locomotive to run on rails was shown to the public. Gas lighting was (11) .... in the streets of London. It was a changing world, both at home and abroad.

0. A If	**B** Because	**C** Since	**D** When
1. A One	**B** That	**C** This	**D** Which
2. A declared	**B** stated	**C** called	**D** pronounced
3. A that	**B** whose	**C** who	**D** which
4. A like	**B** for	**C** as	**D** by
5. A distant	**B** remote	**C** long	**D** far
6. A mention	**B** announcement	**C** talking	**D** revealing
7. A Though	**B** However	**C** Nevertheless	**D** Although
8. A for	**B** in	**C** having	**D** by
9. A put	**B** had	**C** took	**D** made
10. A cancelled	**B** abolished	**C** erased	**D** wiped
11. A presented	**B** offered	**C** introduced	**D** entered

The Battle of Waterloo (*c.* 1824) by George Jones.

INTERNET PROJECT

The Life of the Prince Regent

In 1811, when it became apparent that King George III was no longer able to govern his country, his son, the then Prince of Wales, was appointed Prince Regent. This story is famous and was fantastically retold in the Oscar winning film *The Madness of King George* (1994).

The Prince Regent, who later became George IV, lived a colourful life and was disapproved of by many, including Jane Austen. On the Internet use one of the main search engines to find out more information about his life and then write a report about him.

In particular try to find information about the following topics:

- his first marriage
- his second marriage
- his lifestyle
- his hobbies
- his political views

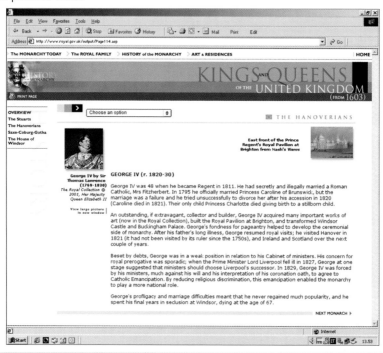

Before you go on

FCE **1** **Listen to the beginning of Part Seven and for questions 1-6 choose the best answers (A, B or C).**

1. Who does Mr Knightley say will invite guests to Donwell?
   A ☐ Mrs Weston.
   B ☐ Mr Knightley himself.
   C ☐ Mr Knightley's wife.

2. Where are they going to eat the strawberries?
   A ☐ In Mr Knightley's dining room.
   B ☐ On a donkey.
   C ☐ Under a tree.

3. What does Mrs Bragge need?
   A ☐ A horse.
   B ☐ A governess.
   C ☐ A job.

4. Who did Emma discover was Mrs Elton's victim?
   A ☐ Emma herself.
   B ☐ Jane Fairfax.
   C ☐ Harriet Smith.

5. What does Jane ask Emma to do for her?
   A ☐ Find her a carriage.
   B ☐ Let her walk by herself.
   C ☐ Tell Mrs Elton to never mention a job with Mrs Bragge again.

6. Why does Emma think that Frank Churchill is in a bad mood?
   A ☐ Because the weather is hot.
   B ☐ Because Jane walked home without a carriage.
   C ☐ Because he wants to leave England.

Part Seven

The Disaster at Box Hill

 Emma had arranged with Mr Weston to visit Box Hill, a well known beauty spot [1] which she had never seen. Mr Weston invited Mrs Elton too. But when one of the horses became lame, [2] the excursion was delayed.

'You had better come to Donwell instead,' said Mr Knightley. 'Come and eat my strawberries.' [3]

Mrs Elton was delighted. 'Name the day, Knightley. I shall choose the guests for you.'

---

1. **beauty spot** : a place famous for its beautiful scenery.
2. **lame** : unable to walk, with a bad leg.
3. **strawberries** : red summer fruit.

The Disaster at Box Hill

'There is only one married woman in the world who I can ever allow to invite guests to Donwell.'

'Mrs Weston, I suppose,' said Mrs Elton, disappointed.

'No – Mrs Knightley. And until she exists, I will invite the guests myself.'

'Ha ha, you are a strange man, Knightley. Well, as it is an open-air party, perhaps I shall come on a donkey. We will gather the strawberries ourselves and sit under the trees to eat them...'

'Not at all. We shall eat in the dining room. Mr Woodhouse would never sit under a tree!'

Under a bright sun on Midsummer's Day, everyone met at Donwell. Emma loved the Abbey.

Mrs Elton led the way to the strawberry fields. She looked ridiculous in a large bonnet [1] and carrying a huge basket.

'My friend Mrs Bragge, who lives near Maple Grove, needs a governess,' she told Jane Fairfax. 'I have told her all about you. You must accept immediately.'

'Let's look at the gardens,' said Jane, wanting to escape.

They looked out over the sweet view of hills, woods, meadows [2] and river. Emma thought that it was the perfect English countryside. Mr Knightley and Harriet were walking together, leading the way.

Emma met Jane Fairfax near the house.

'Please Miss Woodhouse, tell the others that I am going home. I must go.'

'Certainly. But you are not going to walk alone?'

'Yes, I walk fast. I shall be at home in twenty minutes.'

1. **bonnet** : a type of hat which covers the sides of the face and is fastened with strings under the chin.
2. **meadows** : fields with flowers.

'Let me order a carriage. You are tired.'

'Thank you but no. Miss Woodhouse, we all know that sometimes we are wearied [1] in spirit. The greatest kindness will be to leave me alone.'

Emma understood. She suddenly felt deep sympathy for Jane who, with no fortune or rich family, was the victim [2] of Mrs Elton.

Fifteen minutes later, Frank Churchill arrived.

'It is very hot, outside. I am late. I shall soon have to go again. I met Miss Fairfax on the way. Walking. Madness in this hot weather. Madness.'

Emma realised that he was in a bad mood because of the weather.

'As soon as my aunt is well, I shall go abroad, to Switzerland. I want a change. I am serious, Miss Woodhouse – I am sick of England. I would leave tomorrow if I could.'

'We are going to Box Hill tomorrow. Will you join us? It is not Switzerland but it will be a small change for you.'

'Miss Woodhouse, you are my queen. I shall come to Box Hill.' END

The next day was fine. Everyone expected a pleasant excursion. When they arrived, they all agreed that the view was splendid.

Frank Churchill paid great attention to Emma and she, feeling flattered, responded. Soon, it was obvious to everyone that Mr Frank Churchill and Miss Emma Woodhouse were flirting [3] with each other. But he was not winning back Emma's heart.

1. **wearied** : tired.
2. **victim** : a person that is hurt by someone.
3. **flirting** : talking romantically and playfully together.

'Yesterday, I was in a bad mood because I was hot. Today I am cool because I am with you. You are my queen.'

'Since yesterday?'

'Since I first saw you in February.'

'You are very gallant. But we are the only people speaking. It is hard work talking nonsense for the enjoyment of seven silent people.'

'I say nothing that I am ashamed of. [1] I first saw you in February. Let everybody on the hill hear me.' He spoke even more loudly. 'Ladies and gentlemen, Miss Woodhouse orders me to say that she wishes to know what you are thinking about.'

A few people laughed. Mrs Elton was angry because Emma was the 'queen' of the day. Mr Knightley answered very clearly:

'Is Miss Woodhouse sure that she wants to know our thoughts?'

Frank spoke again. 'Ladies and gentlemen, Miss Woodhouse orders me to say that each of you must say one very clever thing. Or two moderately [2] clever things. Or three very stupid things.'

'Oh!' exclaimed Miss Bates. 'Three very stupid things. That will just suit me. [3] I shall be sure to say three very stupid things as soon as I open my mouth.'

Emma could not resist.

'Ah, madam, that may be difficult for you. You will be limited in number – only three at a time.'

There was a sudden silence. For a moment, Miss Bates did not understand the insult. Then she blushed, hurt not angry.

---

1. **ashamed of** : morally embarrassed by, guilty about.
2. **moderately** : not very.
3. **suit me** : be right for me.

'Well,' she said to Mr Knightley, 'I will try to keep quiet. I must be very disagreeable [1] or she would not have said such a thing to an old friend.'

'I have nothing clever to say,' said Mrs Elton.

'Yes, please excuse me also,' said Mr Elton. 'I am an old married man. I have nothing to say that can amuse Miss Woodhouse. Let's go for a walk, Augusta.'

'Yes, Mr E.'

'They are a happy couple,' Frank Churchill said sarcastically. 'They are exactly right for each other. They only knew each other for a few weeks in Bath before they got married. But it is very unusual that you can form a real relationship in a public place like Bath or Weymouth. Many men have got married after knowing somebody for a few weeks and then regretted [2] it for the rest of their lives!'

Jane Fairfax spoke: 'I agree that men and women sometimes make mistakes about each other. But only weak dependent characters will not recover from an unlucky acquaintance [3] of that kind.'

Frank Churchill turned to Emma. 'Well, I hope that somebody will choose my wife for me. Will you, Miss Woodhouse? I am sure I should like your choice. Find somebody for me. And make her like yourself. Adopt [4] her, educate her.'

'Very well, you will have a charming wife.'

1. **disagreeable** : unpleasant.
2. **regretted** : felt sorry for.
3. **unlucky acquaintance** : bad relationship.
4. **adopt** : take a person into someone's family as his/her child.

'She must be very lively – like you – and have hazel [1] eyes – like yours. I shall go abroad for a couple of years. And when I return, I shall come to you for a wife. Remember!'

Emma was thinking of Harriet. Apart from the colour of her eyes, she was the perfect wife for Frank.

'Now, aunt,' said Jane Fairfax, rising quickly, 'let us join Mrs Elton.' She seemed upset.

Then the carriages arrived. The excursion to Box Hill was finished.

Mr Knightley stood by her and spoke quietly. 'Emma, I must speak to you as an old friend. You have behaved very wrongly. How could you be so unkind to Miss Bates?'

Emma laughed. 'I am sure she did not understand me.'

'I know that she did. She has talked to me since then. She is a very unlucky woman, Emma. She is poor, with nothing to look forward to except a lonely old age. You have acted thoughtlessly. [2] Please forgive me, Emma, for speaking so directly.'

They reached the carriage. Before she had time to say anything, she was driven away with Harriet. She felt terribly upset. To her surprise, tears began to run down her cheeks and she did nothing to stop them.

That evening, Emma played cards with her father but she was thinking of Mr Knightley's words. He had

1. **hazel** : light greenish brown in colour.
2. **thoughtlessly** : without thinking about others.

left thinking that she was hard-hearted and proud, before she had time to excuse herself.

Next morning, she went to visit Miss Bates to apologise. When she arrived, Jane went quickly into her bedroom. Emma saw her face briefly – she looked very sad and ill.

'She has a dreadful headache, poor Jane,' said Miss Bates. 'She has been writing to Colonel Campbell and Mrs Dixon with tears in her eyes. Of course, she is very lucky. Mrs Elton has found her a job as a governess with a very good family near Maple Grove. All yesterday, Jane refused to go. But when she came back from Box Hill, Jane said yes.'

'It must be sad for her to leave her friends.'

'She decided everything so very quickly. Mr and Mrs Elton were here. We heard that Mr Churchill had gone back to London. And then, after tea, Jane decided. She cannot take the piano with her, of course. Colonel Campbell will decide what to do.'

When she returned to Hartfield, Emma found Mr Knightley and Harriet there with her father. Mr Knightley immediately got up, looking more serious than usual.

'I came to say goodbye. I am going to London for a few days to visit John and Isabella.'

'But isn't this a sudden plan?'

They stood talking briefly. Emma was sure that he had not forgiven her.

Mr Woodhouse interrupted. 'Well, my dear, did you reach Miss Bates's house safely? Dear Emma has been to call on Mrs and Miss Bates, Mr Knightley. She is always so kind to them.'

Emma blushed. With a smile and a shake of her head, she looked almost shyly at Mr Knightley. His eyes seemed to receive the truth from hers. He said nothing but he forgave her. As he left, he took her hand. He pressed it and seemed about to carry it to his lips. Then, for some reason, he let it go. She felt however that it had been a gesture [1] of perfect friendship. Then he left for London.

Next day, there was astonishing news. Mrs Churchill, Frank's tyrannical [2] aunt, had died.

Emma realised that Frank would now be free to marry whoever he wished. Lucky Harriet. Emma remembered Jane Fairfax's sad face and wrote to her, inviting her to Hartfield. But Jane did not accept, she was too ill. However, later she was seen walking alone in the fields near Highbury. It was clear that she wanted to accept no kindness from Miss Woodhouse.

Suddenly, Mr Weston arrived at Hartfield. 'Emma, you must come to Randalls. Mrs Weston must see you. There is terrible news!'

1. **gesture** : a movement that expresses a feeling.
2. **tyrannical** : cruel, oppressive.

Go back to the text

1 **Are these statements about Part Seven of *Emma* true (T) or false (F)? If there is not enough information to decide, tick possible (P).**

	T	F	P
a. They were unable to go to Box Hill immediately because the coach-horse had a problem.	☐	☐	☐
b. Emma enjoyed looking at the view at Donwell Abbey.	☐	☐	☐
c. Frank Churchill and Emma behaved well at Box Hill.	☐	☐	☐
d. Miss Bates didn't understand Emma's insult.	☐	☐	☐
e. The excursion to Box Hill was more successful than the strawberry party.	☐	☐	☐
f. Emma thought that Mr Knightley was wrong to criticise her.	☐	☐	☐
g. Jane was happy that she had found a job at last.	☐	☐	☐
h. His aunt's death would give Frank more freedom.	☐	☐	☐

2 **What do you think? Why?**

a. What does Mr Knightley say about a future wife?

b. What did Frank and Jane talk about at Box Hill? Did it have a hidden meaning?

c. Is Harriet in love with Frank as Emma thinks?

d. Why did Jane change her mind about the job?

e. What is Mr Weston's bad news?

Had better and would rather

We often use **had better** to give advice. Notice that it refers to the present:
*Harriet **had better stop** thinking about love.*
= Harriet should stop thinking about love.

*Jane **had better not walk** home in this heat.*
= *Jane should not walk home in this heat.*

We use **would rather** to say that we prefer something:
*Frank **would rather live** abroad.* = Frank would prefer to live abroad.
*Mrs Elton **would rather not stay**.* = Mrs Elton would prefer not to stay.

Notice that we do not use **to** before the infinitive with **would rather**,
but we use it after **would prefer**.
The contracted forms of **had better** and **would rather** are **'d better** and
'd rather:
*You**'d better go** now.*
*He**'d rather not go** to the party.*

We often use **would rather have** followed by the **past participle** to
talk about the past, when we are sorry for something.
*She **would rather have gone** to Box Hill alone.*
*Emma **would rather have not insulted** Miss Bates.*

3 **Fill the gaps below with *had better* or *would rather (have)*.**

   a. Harriet .... marry a gentleman than Mr Martin.

   b. Emma .... stop using her imagination.

   c. Mr Elton .... married Emma than Harriet.

   d. Jane Fairfax .... tell Mrs Elton to leave her in peace.

   e. Emma .... apologise to Miss Bates.

   f. John Knightley .... stayed at home than gone to
   Randalls at Christmas.

   g. Frank .... flirt with Emma than talk seriously to Jane.

   h. 'Harriet .... not walk alone in the country again,'
   advised Mr Woodhouse.

   i. 'You .... all eat some lovely gruel.'

   j. 'You .... give us some money,' said the gipsies.

4 Complete the second sentence so that it has a similar meaning to the first sentence using the word given. Do not change the word given. You must use between two and five words, including the word given. There is an example at the beginning.

0. 'Name the day, Mr Knightley,' said Mrs Elton.
told
Mrs Elton **told Mr Knightley to** name the day.

1. I will be home in twenty minutes.
me
It .... minutes to get home.

2. I say nothing that I am ashamed of.
nothing
There .... I am ashamed of.

3. They knew each other for a few weeks before they got married.
after
They got married .... for a few weeks.

4. Only weak dependent characters will not recover from an unlucky acquaintance.
except
Everybody .... from an unlucky acquaintance.

5. 'She has been writing to Colonel Campbell and Mrs Dixon with tears in her eyes,' said Miss Bates.
had
Miss Bates said that she .... to Colonel Campbell and Mrs Dixon with tears in her eyes.

6. It must be sad for her to leave her friends.
sure
I .... sad for her to leave friends.

7. Is Miss Woodhouse sure that she wants to know our thoughts?
what
Is Miss Woodhouse sure that she wants to .... thinking?

Characters

5 **Mr Knightley is one of the most interesting characters in the book. He is intelligent, serious and caring.**
Can you find evidence in the story for the following statements about Mr Knightley?

   a. He watches everything carefully.
   Evidence: *he sees Frank giving the letters B,L,U,N,D,E,R to Jane.*

   b. He often sees the truth before others.
   Evidence: ....

   c. He is like a father to several of the female characters.
   Evidence: ....

   d. He criticises others.
   Evidence: ....

   e. He is very fond of Emma.
   Evidence: ....

   f. Perhaps he is jealous of Frank Churchill.
   Evidence: ....

   g. He finds it difficult to join in the pleasures of the younger people.
   Evidence: ....

   h. He is perhaps Jane Austen's ideal of a perfect gentleman.
   Evidence: ....

6 **What do you think?**

   a. Do you like Mr Knightley?
   b. Would you rather be friends with him or with Frank Churchill?

The Poor

At one point in *Emma*, Miss Woodhouse visits a poor family with sick children to give them advice and help. Later in the story, a gang of gipsy children take money from Harriet. These small incidents remind us that poverty was an increasing part of Jane Austen's England. There were several reasons for this.

The war with France had made life more expensive. Imported food and goods cost more, money had to be raised to finance [1] the war. However, the landowners refused to increase wages. [2] Life became very difficult for the ordinary workers. If they tried to feed their families by catching

Applicants for Admission to a Casual Ward by Sir Luke Fildes.

1. **finance** : provide the money to pay for something.
2. **wages** : money paid to workers weekly.

rabbits or birds in the countryside, they were accused of poaching – stealing from the landowner. There were 'man-traps', [1] iron traps with large teeth, to catch poachers in the private woods.

The Industrial Revolution was also increasing poverty in the countryside. Previously, women had been able to support their families by spinning [2] at home. Blacksmiths [3] worked with metal, carpenters [4] made furniture by hand. Suddenly, these jobs disappeared as the factories produced textiles, iron goods and furniture by machine. As a result, more and more people left the countryside to find jobs in the industrial cities. London was expanding rapidly during these years.

Later in the nineteenth century, Dickens would describe the horrors

Coalbrookdale by Night (1801) by Philip de Loutherbourg.

1. **traps** : things to catch wild animals.
2. **spinning** : making cloth.
3. **blacksmiths** : people who made horseshoes and other iron objects.
4. **carpenters** : people who made things from wood.

of life in large cities as unemployment grew. Even in Jane Austen's time, there were serious riots. ¹ The agitators ² were punished severely with death or transportation to Australia. In 1810 – 1812, a group of men called the 'Luddites' smashed ³ the machinery in the factories. Only two years after Jane's death, the Peterloo Massacre occurred in Manchester when four people were killed and four hundred were injured. There is no sign of this in *Emma* however.

The Peterloo Massacre (detail), a line drawing (1819).

1. **riots** : situations in which people are behaving in a violent and uncontrolled way in the streets.
2. **agitators** : people who cause trouble.
3. **smashed** : broke violently into many pieces.

1 **Decide if these statements are true (T) or false (F). Then correct the false ones.**

		T	F
a.	Jane Austen gives us a picture of the whole of English society.	☐	☐
b.	Ordinary people in the countryside were becoming richer.	☐	☐
c.	The Industrial Revolution threatened traditional English country life.	☐	☐
d.	There were strong punishments for people who protested.	☐	☐

Before you go on

FCE

1 **Listen to the beginning of Part Eight, and decide whether the statements are true (T) or false (F).**

		T	F
1.	Emma had no idea why Mrs Weston wanted to talk to her.	☐	☐
2.	Frank Churchill can now marry Jane Fairfax because Mr Churchill is dead.	☐	☐
3.	Frank and Jane have been secretly engaged for the past nine months.	☐	☐
4.	Emma was beginning to fall in love with Frank Churchill.	☐	☐
5.	Mrs Weston did not want Emma to marry Frank Churchill.	☐	☐
6.	Harriet was never in love with Frank Churchill.	☐	☐
7.	Harriet is now in love with Mr Knightley.	☐	☐
8.	Emma suddenly realises that Mr Knightley must marry her.	☐	☐

Part Eight

The Autumn Marriages

 hat is wrong?' asked Emma as they walked quickly
to Randalls. 'Is Mrs Weston ill?'

'No, nothing of the kind. She will tell you herself.
I promised I would let her break it to you.' [1]

'Good God!' said Emma, suddenly terrified. 'Is it my sister and
her family? Are they ill?'

'No, it has nothing to do with them. Be patient.'

They arrived at Randalls. 'Mrs Weston, my dear, I have
brought her. I shall leave you together. She has not the least idea.'

'My dear friend,' said Emma. 'Tell me quickly. What is the
trouble?'

'Have you no idea?'

'None.'

---

1. **break it to you** : tell you the bad news.

'Well, Frank visited us this morning. He came to tell his father that...'

'Yes?'

'...that he has been secretly engaged to Jane Fairfax for the last nine months.'

'Jane Fairfax! Good God! You are not serious?'

'Yes. They fell in love at Weymouth and have kept it a secret from everybody. Now that Mrs Churchill is dead, they can tell the world.'

'Poor Harriet,' thought Emma.

'He has hurt me and hurt his father. Why did he keep it a secret from us? But most of all we are afraid that he has behaved very badly towards you.'

'I understand. But dear Mrs Weston,' said Emma sincerely, 'I have really cared nothing about him these last three months. That is the simple truth.'

Mrs Weston kissed her with tears of joy. 'It was our dearest wish for you and Frank to be married. But I am so glad that you have not been in love yourself.'

'I have escaped. But that does not excuse him. He tried to please me, to make me fall in love with him. He was deceiving [1] me and hurting Jane.'

'Yes, he knows that he has behaved improperly. [2] He quarrelled with Jane and he reacted stupidly at Box Hill.'

'Oh, Mrs Weston, he did not behave like a man of honour. He used tricks instead of depending on the truth.'

---

1. **deceiving** : tricking, cheating.
2. **improperly** : wrongly, badly.

'But he has many good qualities, my dear. They have both suffered [1] a great deal by keeping their relationship secret. Now, Mr Churchill, his uncle, will permit the marriage.'

Mr Weston returned. Emma laughed. 'I congratulate you, Mr Weston, with all my heart, on having one of the most lovely and talented young women in England as your future daughter-in-law.'

When Emma returned to Hartfield, she saw Harriet.

'Isn't the news strange?' said Harriet. 'Frank Churchill and Jane Fairfax.'

Emma was surprised. She did not seem upset.

'I am very glad for Jane,' said Emma. 'But I am sorry that I did not realise the truth and warn you.'

'Warn me? Do you think that I care about Frank Churchill? I am in love with a far superior gentleman.'

'Who do you mean, Harriet?'

'Mr Knightley, of course!'

'But Frank Churchill rescued you from the gipsies.'

'And Mr Knightley rescued me from the Eltons by dancing with me at the ball. That was a noble, kind, generous action. He is the best gentleman on the earth.'

'Good God!' cried Emma.

'I suppose, Miss Woodhouse, that you think that Mr Knightley is too far above me. But if I am fortunate, if he returns my love, I hope you will not put difficulties in the way.'

'Do you think that Mr Knightley is in love with you?'

'Yes,' replied Harriet. 'I have seen signs.'

---

1. **suffered** : felt pain.

Emma dropped her eyes and sat silently for a few minutes. She looked into her own heart. She made rapid progress, arriving suddenly at [1] the whole truth. It darted [2] through her, with the speed of an arrow, that Mr Knightley must marry no one but herself.

END

Harriet talked about Mr Knightley. They had danced at the ball, walked together at the strawberry party, sat next to each other at Hartfield. Emma remembered his words at the ball: 'She is a natural modest girl that any man...'

'At Donwell, he asked me if I was in love with anyone.'

'Perhaps he was asking for his friend Robert Martin.'

'No!' said Harriet firmly. 'He did not mention Mr Martin. I care nothing for Mr Martin. Dear Miss Woodhouse, tell me, do you think he loves me?'

'He is the best person in the world,' said Emma. 'That is all I can say.'

Emma was completely confused. She knew that she had been blind to the feelings of others and to her own heart. When had Mr Knightley become so dear to her? She compared Frank Churchill and Mr Knightley. She had always thought Mr Knightley superior, she had never really cared for Frank Churchill. She had behaved very badly. She had encouraged Harriet to fall in love with the wrong men, she had believed herself in the secret of everyone's feelings, she had tried to arrange other people's lives. And she herself had made Harriet vain and independent enough to dream of being the mistress of Donwell Abbey.

---

1. **arriving suddenly at** : (here) suddenly understanding.
2. **darted** : passed very quickly.

Emma had never known before how much her happiness depended on being first with Mr Knightley, first in interest and affection. She remembered how often they had quarrelled. But still he had loved her and watched over [1] her. In spite of her faults, she knew that she was dear to him. But he had been very angry with her at Box Hill.

The weather was dull and wet and Mr Woodhouse was unhappy. She had to amuse him constantly. But in the afternoon, the rain cleared and there was calm sunlight. She went into the garden and walked around it once or twice. Then she saw Mr Knightley. He had returned from London!

He looked worried. Had he told his brother that he wanted to marry Harriet? Did Mr Knightley now want to talk to Emma about his love for Harriet?

'I have some news which will surprise you,' she said.

'If it is about Jane Fairfax and Frank Churchill, then I have already heard,' he replied.

'You were probably not surprised. You tried to tell me that they had an understanding. But I was blind.' She sighed heavily.

He took her arm in his and pressed her hand against his chest. 'Time, my dearest Emma, will heal [2] the wound. The abominable scoundrel! [3] He doesn't deserve her.'

Emma realised what he thought. 'You are very kind but you are mistaken. I was blind and I did some silly things. But I am glad that he and Jane are together. I never loved him.'

'Emma!' he cried, looking into her eyes.

---

1. **watched over** : guarded or protected.
2. **heal** : make better, cure.
3. **abominable scoundrel** : a disgusting and dishonest man.

'I may have given the wrong impression but I have never been attached to Frank Churchill. I enjoyed flirting with him. Now I understand that he was hiding his true feelings behind his attentions to me. But I was always safe from him.'

'Well,' said Mr Knightley, 'he is a fortunate man. He is going to marry one of the best of women. I envy him...'

'Is he going to speak about Harriet?' thought Emma.

'Emma, I want to tell you why I envy Frank Churchill. I cannot be wise, Emma. I must tell you what I feel, although I may wish it unsaid the next moment.'

'Then don't speak,' she said quickly. He must not tell her about Harriet.

He was silent. Emma could see that he was suffering. As a friend, she ought to give him support in his love for Harriet. 'I stopped you ungraciously [1] just now. But if you wish to speak to me as a friend, I shall listen.'

'As a 'friend'?' repeated Mr Knightley. 'No, Emma, not only as a friend. No, I have gone too far. Tell me then, have I no chance of ever succeeding?'

He stopped. The expression of his eyes made her feel weak.

'My dearest Emma, tell me at once. Say 'no' if you must. You are silent. I ask no more.'

Emma was afraid to believe the truth.

'I cannot make speeches, [2] Emma. If I loved you less, I might be able to speak about it more. All these years, I have told you the truth about yourself and you have borne [3] it as no other woman in

---

1. **ungraciously** : impolitely.
2. **make speeches** : speak like a public speaker, express your ideas skilfully.
3. **borne** : tolerated, put up with.

England would have borne it. But you also have wonderful qualities...'

Emma suddenly understood the whole truth. Harriet had been mistaken. Harriet was nothing to him. She herself, Emma Woodhouse, was everything. She told him what she had discovered about her own heart.

Mr Knightley was amazed. He had come unselfishly to comfort Emma for the loss of Frank Churchill. Within half an hour, he had passed from the greatest depression [1] to perfect happiness.

So Emma agreed to marry Mr Knightley. 'You must call me George,' he said.

'But I have called you 'Mr Knightley' all my life. I shall call you 'George' in the church. But while my father lives, I cannot leave Hartfield to live at Donwell Abbey. It must be a long engagement.'

'Then I shall come to live here at Hartfield.'

Mrs Weston showed them a long letter from Frank Churchill explaining his behaviour. He apologised to everyone and admitted his mistakes. He should not have flirted with Miss Woodhouse. He should not have embarrassed Jane by sending her the piano as a gift. But luckily, everything had ended happily. 'I am the child of good fortune,' he wrote.

'What will Harriet do now?' wondered Emma. 'Even Harriet cannot fall in love with more than three men in one year!' But Robert Martin still loved her; when he asked her again to marry him, she accepted gladly.

All Highbury was talking about the engagement of Miss Woodhouse and Mr Knightley. 'Poor Knightley,' said Mrs Elton.

1. **depression** : sadness.

But everybody else was happy. Except Mr Woodhouse. 'I am no friend to marriage,' he said. 'Poor Miss Taylor. Poor Isabella. Do not get married, my dear.'

Luckily, somebody in the area stole some chickens and turkeys from the Westons during the night. Other houses were robbed. 'If Mr Knightley lives at Hartfield, papa,' said Emma cleverly, 'he can protect us. We can sleep well at night.' So even Mr Woodhouse was glad that Emma was going to get married.

In September, Harriet and Robert Martin were married. In November, Jane and Frank Churchill were married. In October, the wedding of Miss Emma Woodhouse, the mistress of Hartfield, and Mr George Knightley, the master of Donwell, took place. It was a small wedding. Mrs Elton's wedding, she said, had been much grander. But the small number of true friends who witnessed the ceremony knew that the marriage was one of perfect happiness.

Go back to the text

1 **Are these statements about Part Eight of *Emma* true (T) or false (F)? If there is not enough information to decide, tick possible (P).**

		T	F	P
a.	Mrs Weston sent her husband to tell Emma the news.	☐	☐	☐
b.	Frank and Jane had been in love before he came to Highbury.	☐	☐	☐
c.	Emma was heart-broken by the news about Jane and Frank.	☐	☐	☐
d.	Emma really began to believe that Mr Knightley loved Harriet.	☐	☐	☐
e.	Emma realised that she loved Mr Knightley herself.	☐	☐	☐
f.	Mr Knightley came back from London to see Harriet.	☐	☐	☐
g.	Mr Knightley found it difficult to express his feelings.	☐	☐	☐
h.	Mr Woodhouse agreed to the marriage because he wanted Emma to be happy.	☐	☐	☐

Looking back

2 **Jane Austen gave us lots of clues to the secret engagement. Look back through the story and see how many you can find. For example:**

– Page 99 : Frank took a pair of scissors to Miss Bates's house when he was leaving – really he wanted to say goodbye to Jane.

There are also lots of clues to the deep affection between Emma and Mr Knightley. Can you find them? For example:

– Page 25 : Mr Knightley tells Mrs Weston that Emma is one of the most attractive women he has seen.

– Page 70 : When it is possible that he loves Jane, Emma is confused – she doesn't want him to marry.

Should / shouldn't have

Frank writes:

*I **should not have flirted** with Miss Woodhouse.*
*I **should not have embarrassed** Jane.*

We use **should have** or **shouldn't have** when we are looking back on the past. It is too late to change things. For example:

*I **should have studied** harder for the exam.*

3 Use 'should have' or 'shouldn't have' to comment on the actions of the characters. There is an example at the beginning.

    a. Emma told Harriet that Mr Martin was not good enough for her.

    She shouldn't have told Harriet that Mr Martin wasn't good enough for her.

    b. Emma insulted Miss Bates.

    c. Frank sent Jane a piano in secret.

    d. Frank flirted with Emma.

    e. Frank didn't make his engagement to Jane in public until his aunt died.

    f. Jane hid her engagement with Frank Churchill from everybody.

    g. Jane didn't accept Emma's kind gestures.

    h. Harriet turned down Mr Martin's marriage proposal.

    i. Harriet listened to all of Emma's advice.

    j. Mr Elton refused to dance with Harriet in order to hurt Emma.

    k. Mr Knightley never told Emma that he loved her.

    l. Mr Churchill let his wife control Frank's life.

Listening

🎧 **4** **Listen to Part Eight of *Emma*. As you listen, can you complete the quotations given below?**

a. It was our dearest wish ....
.... (7 words)

b. I congratulate you, Mr Weston, with all my heart, on having one
of the ....
.... (12 words)

c. It darted through her, with the speed of an arrow, ...
.... (8 words)

d. Emma had never known before how much her happiness depended
on being ....
.... (9 words)

e. If I loved you less, ...
.... (9 words)

f. I have told you the truth about yourself and you have borne it
.... (10 words)

g. 'I ....
....,' he wrote. (6 words)

h. Even Harriet cannot ....
.... (11 words)

These eight quotations are all Jane Austen's original words.

Characters

5 **When Jane Austen chose Emma Woodhouse as the heroine of her novel, she wrote that no one except herself would like her.**
It is true that Miss Emma Woodhouse has many faults. Can you find evidence for these?

a. She is snobbish.
Evidence: *Page 22 she does not like Mr Martin because he is a farmer.*

b. She is cruel or inconsiderate to others.

Evidence: ....

c. She interferes in the lives of other people.

Evidence: ....

d. She loves to be the centre of attention.

Evidence: ....

e. She doesn't listen to good advice.

Evidence: ....

f. She is spoilt and lazy.

Evidence: ....

g. She doesn't learn from experience.
Evidence: ....

Can you add more faults? So why do many readers like her? In fact, when I first read *Emma*, I fell in love with her.
Have you also enjoyed reading about Miss Emma Woodhouse?

The Upper Classes

The world of *Emma* exists outside the general change and unrest. [1] The upper classes protected themselves by creating a highly controlled world with clear class distinctions. [2] Emma herself is an unashamed [3] snob. She will not mix with Mr Martin, the farmer. She only agrees to visit the Coles because she wants to dance with Frank Churchill. There is a clear difference in her mind between the traditional families – the Woodhouses and the Knightleys – and the newly rich business families, – the Coles and the relatives of Augusta Hawkins of Bristol. It is even possible that the money of the Hawkins family came from slavery [4] as Bristol was a centre of the slave trade.

Mr Knightley seems to have more liberal ideas than Emma but he does nothing to change the class distinctions which exist. The country gentlemen and ladies lived a very formal artificial [5] life. We can see in *Emma* that even between friends first names were rarely used. Emma has known Mr Knightley all her life but even when they are engaged she finds it impossible to call him 'George'. It is a world of good manners and pleasant civilised living.

There is an almost invisible population of characters in *Emma* – the servants. Isabella needed nurses to look after her five children. At the dinners and parties, the food is prepared by cooks, the fires are lit by servants, the carriages are driven by coachmen. Jane Austen never gives these people a voice in her novels. Perhaps she realised

---

1. **unrest** : anxiety, confusion.
2. **distinctions** : differences.
3. **unashamed** : not sorry for.
4. **slavery** : buying and selling people.
5. **artificial** : not true or sincere.

that she did not know how they thought or spoke and that she should concentrate on the world she knew.

Thus, there was a hidden side to Jane Austen's England. However, this shouldn't make us forget the positive side. *Emma* shows us a small intimate [1] society where people like Miss Bates, Harriet and Jane Fairfax receive kindness and support from others. It was a world under threat from the changes taking place throughout Europe but it was a world that we can still inhabit [2] thanks to Jane Austen's talents as a writer.

The Cloakroom at Clifton Assembly Rooms (*c.* 1819), by Rolinda Sharples.

1. **intimate** : private, personal.
2. **inhabit** : live in.

1 Decide if these statements are true (T) or false (F). Then correct the false ones.

	T	F
a. Mr Knightley destroys class distinctions.	☐	☐
b. The newly rich families were accepted as equal by the traditional families.	☐	☐
c. Servants were an essential part of Jane Austen's society.	☐	☐
d. People like Miss Bates were treated badly.	☐	☐

T: GRADE 8

2 Topic – Society
Find a picture or photo of a famous or very rich person in your country. Think about how they and other wealthy people live today.
Use the following questions to help you.

a. Where do they live?

b. What type of work do they do?

c. What are the advantages of this type of lifestyle?

d. How would your life have been different if you had been born into a family similar to Emma's?

EXIT TEST

1 **Secret Loves**

a. Many of Frank's and Jane's actions can now be explained in the light of their secret engagement. Give four examples:

....
....
....

b. What clues does Jane Austen give us that Emma is actually in love with Mr Knightley?

....
....
....

c. What clues does Jane Austen give us that Mr Knightley is in love with Emma?

....
....
....

d. How is the mystery of the love between Frank and Jane different from the mystery of the love between Emma and Mr Knightley?

....
....
....

2 **Defects**

What are the main character defects of:

- Emma
- Frank Churchill
- Mrs Elton
- Harriet
- Jane Fairfax
- Mr Woodhouse

3 Love and marriage
In *Emma* Jane Austen gives us a good picture of marriage among the upper classes of the English countryside at the beginning of the nineteenth century.

What was the importance of:

a. money;

b. social position;

c. love;

d. moral character of the person?

4 Marrying for Survival

a. How does Jane Austen show us that marriage was not just a question of love for many women?

b. Is Emma's situation more or less difficult than that of Jane Fairfax? Or of Harriet Smith?

5 A Good Marriage and a Bad Marriage
Jane Austen seems to present Emma and Mr Knightley's marriage as a perfect union, while she does not seem to approve of that of Mr Elton and Miss Augusta Hawkins.

a. What are the differences between these two couples?

b. What do they have in common?

1. What was Mr Elton's occupation?

    A ☐ He was a farmer.
    B ☐ He was the master of a large estate.
    C ☐ He was an important merchant.
    D ☐ He was a vicar.

2. Who was Harriet Smith?

    A ☐ Emma's governess.
    B ☐ An orphan who lived at the local school.
    C ☐ An orphan who worked at the vicarage.
    D ☐ A friend of Mr Woodhouse.

3. What did Emma want to do for Harriet?

    A ☐ Find her a job as a teacher.
    B ☐ Instruct her and give her good manners.
    C ☐ Teach her to paint.
    D ☐ Prevent her from marrying Mr Elton, whom Emma considered a poor match.

4. Why doesn't Emma want Harriet to marry Mr Martin?

    A ☐ Because he does not write well.
    B ☐ Because he does not have gentlemanly manners.
    C ☐ Because he is a farmer who works for Mr Knightley.
    D ☐ Because he only thinks of money.

5. How does Emma interpret Mr Elton's compliments on her portrait of Harriet?

    A ☐ As proof of her artistic talent.
    B ☐ As proof that Mr Elton is in love with her.
    C ☐ As proof that Mr Elton has good manners.
    D ☐ As proof that Mr Elton is in love with Harriet.

6. How does Emma interpret Mr Martin's desire to marry Harriet?

    A ☐ He only wants to improve his social position.
    B ☐ He is truly in love with Harriet.
    C ☐ He needs somebody to help him with his house.
    D ☐ He has poor judge of character if he wants to marry such a simple girl as Harriet.

7. When does Emma finally understand that Mr Elton is in love with her and not with Harriet?

A ☐ When he smiles even though Harriet is ill.

B ☐ When he does not ask Harriet to marry him during Harriet's visit at the vicarage.

C ☐ When he ignores Harriet at the dance.

D ☐ When he asks Emma to marry him during their carriage ride.

8. What does Emma think is the real reason that Jane Fairfax came to stay with her aunt in Highbury?

A ☐ To be close to Miss Bates.

B ☐ To forget her love for Mr Dixon.

C ☐ To find a husband.

D ☐ To find a job as a governess.

9. Why does Mr Knightley say that he would not marry Jane Fairfax?

A ☐ Because she does not have an open personality.

B ☐ Because she is an orphan.

C ☐ Because she is in love with Mr Dixon.

D ☐ Because she plays the piano well but does not show much taste.

10. Why does Mr Knightley really criticise Frank Churchill?

A ☐ Because he believes that Emma is in love with him.

B ☐ Because he believes that Jane is in love with him.

C ☐ Because he is envious of his high social position.

D ☐ Because he does not think he should have hidden his engagement with Jane.

11. Why does Emma begin to think that Mr Knightley is in love with Jane?

A ☐ Because Mrs Weston put the idea in her head.

B ☐ Because Mr Knightley needs a wife and Jane is available.

C ☐ Because Mr Knightley loves music.

D ☐ Because Mr Knightley lent Miss Bates and Jane his carriage.

12. Why did Emma not want to go to the Coles' party?

A ☐ Because she did not want to dance with Mr Elton.

B ☐ Because the Coles were only interested in money.

C ☐ Because she considered the Coles her social inferiors.

D ☐ Because the Coles were terrible snobs.

13. What is a barouche-landau?

   A ☐ An expensive kind of French fabric.
   B ☐ A fashionable kind of French wine.
   C ☐ A fashionable kind of carriage.
   D ☐ An expensive and fashionable dessert.

14. What does Mrs Elton advise Jane Fairfax to do?

   A ☐ Go to Mr Dixon in Ireland.
   B ☐ Marry Mr Frank Churchill.
   C ☐ Get a job teaching piano.
   D ☐ Get a job as a governess.

15. Why did Emma think that Harriet was in love with Frank Churchill?

   A ☐ Because he saved her from Mrs Elton's cruelty.
   B ☐ Because he saved her from drowning.
   C ☐ Because he saved her from the gipsies.
   D ☐ Because he was very wealthy.

16. How does Mr Knightley guess that Frank Churchill is in love with Jane?

   A ☐ Frank knew that Mr Perry wanted to buy a carriage.
   B ☐ He saw Frank go out with an umbrella for Jane.
   C ☐ He knew that Frank would not go all the way to London just for a hair-cut.
   D ☐ He thought it strange that Jane wanted to walk to get her letters.

17. Why was Emma angry with Frank Churchill when she discovered that he was going to marry Jane Fairfax?

   A ☐ Because she wanted to marry him.
   B ☐ Because he had deceived her.
   C ☐ Because she did not think a trifling young man like him was good enough for Jane.
   D ☐ Because she thought he was foolish to marry a young woman without a family and money.

KEY TO THE ACTIVITIES

Page 14 – exercise 1

a. He was an Anglican clergyman.
b. She was educated at home.
c. She wanted to amuse her family.
d. A comic history of the world and several unpublished novels.
e. By a lady.
f. Love and marriage.
g. Love is an important ingredient of a successful marriage but financial security, comfort, shared beliefs and opinions are equally important.
h. She never found the man whom she wanted to marry.
i. The French Revolution, the Napoleonic Wars, the birth of the United States as a nation, the beginnings of the Industrial Revolution.
j. She preferred to describe the personal lives of her characters.

Page 16 – exercise 1

1. A   2. C   3. C   4. A   5. B   6. C

Part One

Page 26 – exercise 1

1. B   2. A   3. B   4. A   5. D   6. D
7. A   8. B   9. C   10. A

Page 26 – exercise 2

Open answers.

Page 27 – exercise 3

a. 'I will come to see you,' Emma said.
b. Mr Knightley said that he had been to London to visit his brother's family.
c. Emma stated that she herself had made the match.
d. 'I am very sad about the wedding,' said Mr Woodhouse.
e. Mr Woodhouse told Emma that it was a dangerous thing to do.
f. 'We went to London for the holidays,' Mr Weston said.
g. Emma declared that she would look for a wife for Mr Elton.
h. 'Miss Taylor is getting married,' he told me.
i. 'I stayed with the Martins last summer,' Harriet told her.
j. Harriet exclaimed that she was so lucky to meet him.

Page 28 – exercise 4

Open answer.

Page 28 – exercise 5

Open answers.

Page 29 – exercise 6

Open answer.

Page 30 – exercise 7

1. A 2. B 3. C 4. A 5. D 6. C
7. D 8. A 9. C 10. D 11. A 12. B

Page 32 – exercise 1

1. B 2. D 3. B 4. A 5. C 6. A
7. C 8. A 9. D 10. D

Page 32 – exercise 2

Open answers.

Part Two

Page 42 – exercise 1

1. B 2. D 3. D 4. C 5. B 6. A

Page 43 – exercise 2

Open answers.

Page 44 – exercise 3

a. He is getting his picture taken.
b. I will have my house painted.
c. We got our computer repaired last week.
d. She has had her wisdom teeth removed.
e. I get my car serviced every six months.

Page 44 – exercise 4

a. had it filled
b. had it shortened
c. get it cut
d. will have my eyes tested

e. have it installed
f. get them lengthened

Page 45 – exercise 5

Possible answer:
Dearest Sarah,
Do you remember how we used to talk together about marriage when we were in the orphanage together. Well, you won't believe it but someone has asked me to marry him! His name is Mr Martin and I met him on his farm last summer. He has always been very kind to me. Just think last summer he rode three miles just to get me some walnuts. Well, I should be happy, I suppose, but my dear friend Emma Woodhouse, the mistress of Hartfield, thinks that he is not good enough for me, and that it would be difficult for her to see me if I married him. So, I told him no. I think this is the right decision because I am going to marry Mr Elton, the vicar. But if Mr Elton does not want to marry me, and I have turned down such a kind and good man as Mr Martin, now that would be truly horrible!
Your old and still loyal friend,
Harriet Smith

Page 45 – exercise 5

Open answers.

Jane Austen and Reading

Page 48 – exercise 1

a. T
b. F – She also read contemporary works of fiction.
c. F – It is one of Jane Austen's earlier novels.
d. T

e. F – The Romantics generally preferred passion and imagination whereas Jane Austen preferred calmness and reason.

f. F – They generally liked wild landscapes.

g. T

h. T

i. T

Page 48 – exercise 1

Open answer.

Part Three

Page 57 – exercise 1

A 8   **B** 1   **C** 4   **D** 2   **E** 3   **F** 6
G not used   **H** 5   **I** 7

Page 57 – exercise 2

Possible answers:

a. The first clear indication was when Mr Elton does not ask Harriet to marry him during their visit to the vicarage. The second is when Mr Elton shows no interest in Harriet's sore throat.

b. It shows us that once she has an idea about people she does not let reality upset this idea. She is blinded by her own imagination.

c. She feels a strong connection with him because he too is young, attractive and comes from an important family. He is the most eligible young man she knows and she is an eligible young woman.

d. She thinks that she must be in love with Mr Dixon because he once saved her life, and that now Jane is running away from a broken heart. Once again, Emma is influenced by her imagination: for her, if a man saves your life –

like in a romantic novel – then you must fall in love with him.

e. He is greatly annoyed.

f. Yes, it does. Because, as Mr Knightley said, she has more imagination than understanding. She forms her opinions on what her imaginative ideas of love are and tends to ignore how people actually act.

Page 58 – exercise 3

a. were eating
b. had been crying
c. had been driving
d. had been baking
e. was talking / had been drinking
f. had been snowing
g. was looking for
h. was running
i. was walking / had been swimming
j. was talking

Page 60 – exercise 4

1. when   **2.** an   **3.** had   **4.** no   **5.** for
6. where   **7.** in   **8.** too   **9.** was
10. part   **11.** could   **12.** wears
13. however / though   **14.** used
15. one

Page 62 – exercise 5

						12		
1	P	O	R	T	R	A	I	T
2	H	A	N	D	S	O	M	E
3			M	A	T	C	H	
4		D	A	U	G	H	T	E	R
5	A	S	T	O	N	I	S	H	E	D
6	P	L	A	I	N			
7		H	E	A	L	T	H	
8	G	E	N	T	L	E	M	A	N
9		V	I	C	A	R		
10	S	P	O	I	L	T		
11	O	R	P	H	A	N		

Page 63 – exercise 1

1. T
2. F – They visited for fourteen minutes.
3. T
4. F – She cannot allow Harriet to fall in love in with Robert Martin.
5. T
6. T
7. F – He visited the Bates's house after visiting Emma.
8. F – He met Miss Fairfax in Weymouth, but she is now in Highbury.

Page 63 – exercise 2

Open answers.

Part Four

Page 72 – exercise 1

a. He wants to organise a ball there.
b. He buys himself a pair of gloves.
c. Because Mr Dixon always asked her to play the piano.
d. To have a haircut.
e. They thought it was frivolous to leave his father just to have a haircut.
f. Because the Coles were from too low a social class for Emma, but Frank Churchill would be there, and there would be dancing.
g. Jane had received a piano as a present, but no one knew who had given it to her.
h. Because she had a strange hairstyle.
i. Because she would become the mistress of Donwell Abbey, and her sister, Isabella, would not inherit it.
j. That he is a 'trifling silly young fellow'.

Page 72 – exercise 2

Open answers.

Page 73 – exercise 3

1. f / If John Knightley had got in the right carriage, Mr Elton would not have proposed.
2. g / If Emma had had more understanding, she would have guessed that Mr Elton was in love with her.
3. b / If Mr Weston's first wife had not died, Mr Woodhouse would have been happier.
4. a / If Mr Dixon had not saved Jane, she would have drowned.
5. e / If Emma had accepted Mr Elton's marriage proposal, he would not have married Augusta Hawkins.
6. c / If his aunt had let him, he (Frank) would have come to Highbury more often.

Page 74 – exercise 4

Possible answer:

Last night your Highbury high-society reporter attended the lovely party thrown by the Cole family. As my readers will surely remember, the Coles were once poor but now they are now as wealthy as any family in town because their business has done so well. Their party was a real success too, and not even Highbury's elite dared not come.

Who were the king and queen of this splendid evening? Well, the queen was either Highbury's own Emma Woodhouse who was as lovely as ever, or the newcomer, Miss Jane Fairfax who is as talented as she is beautiful. The king, with no doubt, was the fashionable and charming Mr Frank Churchill, who sang and danced with the evening's two queenly maidens. But the evening was even more exceptional because of a great mystery: a piano was sent to the lovely Miss Jane Fairfax as a gift. Who sent it? Nobody knows for sure, but your reporter heard some say that it was Mr Dixon, who once saved Miss Fairfax from drowning. How romantic! Unfortunately for Miss Fairfax, Mr Dixon is no longer available. So was this piano given as a kind souvenir of a past love? Of course, we will try to find the answer for our loyal readers.

Page 75 – exercise 5
Open answers.

Page 76 – exercise 6
Open answers.

Page 76 – exercise 7
Open answers.

Leisure in Early Nineteenth-Century England

Page 80 – exercise 1
a. Bath, Weymouth, London, Southend and other seaside resorts.
b. Boat excursions.
c. Take baths in natural spring water.
d. Neo-classical.
e. At seaside towns.
f. For their health.
g. Separate areas for men and for women.
h. Horse-drawn carriages that took people down to the water so others would not see them in their bathing costumes.

i. Women who helped people into the sea.

Part Five

Page 87 – exercise 1
1. C **2.** D **3.** D **4.** C **5.** A

Page 88 – exercise 2
Open answers.

Page 88 – exercise 3
(first part)
a. put up with – tolerate
b. put off – postpone
c. break off – end
d. fed up with – be tired of
e. brought up – raised
f. show off – act in a way to attract the attention of others

Page 88 – exercise 3
(second part)
a. bring up
b. show off
c. put off
d. put up with this
e. fed up with
f. broken off

Page 89 – exercise 4
Possible answers:
a. Because he was in the same room with the woman he had desired to marry, the woman he had been expected to marry and the woman whom he had actually married.
b. Mrs Elton is wearing a very garish red and pink dress with pink fancy trim. She is constantly moving her hands in wide, self-important arcs. She feels quite good.
Emma is wearing a simple but

elegant off-white Empire-line dress with a simple robin's-egg blue ribbon under the bosom. She is feeling annoyed and is saying little except, 'Yes, of course,' 'Certainly,' and other similar expressions to hide her annoyance. Mr Elton is wearing a chocolate-brown tailcoat and champagne-coloured trousers. He is holding his hands behind his back to hide his nervousness. He says practically nothing but, 'Yes' or 'Oh' because his embarrassment makes it impossible for him to say anything else.

c. Vain, self-satisfied, self-important, ignorant, rude, ill-mannered.
d. Modest, unpretentious, unassuming, well-bred, polite, well-mannered
e. French
f. Four. Because she is very proud of the fact that they have this costly means of transport.
g. For Mr Woodhouse's health, and so that Emma can meet members of the 'best society'.

Page 89 – exercise 5

Open answers.

Page 90 – exercise 6

1. ✓ 2. been 3. ✓ 4. ✓ 5. the
6. off 7. ✓ 8. ✓ 9. an 10. to 11. ✓
12. as 13. ✓ 14. about 15. that
16. ✓ 17. ✓ 18. along 19. doesn't
20. ✓ 21. been 22. this

Page 92 – exercise 1

1. she was jealous.
2. a walk before breakfast does her good.
3. delicate plants.
4. a governess.
5. until she sees the Campbells in London that summer.
6. had decided to come to London.
7. soon meet Frank.
8. make the most noise.
9. went out with an umbrella to protect them from the rain.
10. was talking continuously.

Page 92 – exercise 2

Open answers.

Part Six

Page 102 – exercise 1

1. B 2. D 3. E 4. D 5. D 6. C 7. C
8. B 9. D

Page 102 – exercise 2

Open answer.

Page 103 – exercise 3

1. While 2. so 3. when 4. because
5. although 6. As 7. Before 8. and
9. After 10. If 11. since

Page 104 – exercise 4

wealth / poverty
affection / dislike
kind / cruel
expensive / inexpensive
good-looking / ugly
polite / rude
fashionable / unfashionable
reserved / open
frivolous / serious
handsome / unattractive
thoughtful / thoughtless
warmly / coldly
uncertain / certain
mistaken / right
accept / reject

cruelly / kindly
good-natured / bad-natured
superior / inferior

Page 105 – exercise 5

Open answers.

Page 106 – exercise 6

1. C **2.** A **3.** B **4.** C **5.** D **6.** A
7. D **8.** A **9.** C **10.** B **11.** C

Page 109 – exercise 1

1. B **2.** A **3.** B **4.** B **5.** B **6.** A

Part Seven

Page 119 – exercise 1

a. T **b.** T **c.** F **d.** F **e.** F **f.** F **g.** P
h. T

Page 119 – exercise 2

Open answers.

Page 120 – exercise 3

a. would rather
b. had better
c. would rather have
d. had better
e. had better
f. would rather have
g. would rather
h. had better
i. had better
j. had better

Page 121 – exercise 4

1. It will take me twenty minutes to get home.
2. There is nothing I say that I am ashamed of
3. They got married after having known each other for a few weeks.
4. Everybody except weak dependent characters recovers from an unlucky acquaintance.
5. Miss Bates said that she had been writing to Colonel Campbell and Mrs Dixon with tears in her eyes.
6. I am sure that it is sad for her to leave friends.
7. Is Miss Woodhouse sure that she wants to know what we are thinking?

Page 122 – exercise 5

Open answers.

Page 122 – exercise 6

Open answers.

The Poor

Page 126 – exercise 1

a. F – She only portrays upper-class life.
b. F – They were becoming poorer because of the Industrial Revolution.
c. T
d. T

Page 126 – exercise 1

1. T **2.** F **3.** T **4.** F **5.** F **6.** T **7.** T
8. T

Part Eight

Page 137 – exercise 1

a. T **b.** T **c.** F **d.** T **e.** T **f.** F **g.** T
h. F

Page 137 – exercise 2

Open answers.

Page 138 – exercise 3

b. Emma shouldn't have insulted Miss Bates.

c. Frank shouldn't have sent Jane a piano in secret.

d. Frank shouldn't have flirted with Emma.

e. Frank should have made his engagement to Jane in public before his aunt died.

f. Jane shouldn't have hidden her engagement with Frank Churchill from everybody.

g. Jane should have accepted Emma's kind gestures.

h. Harriet shouldn't have turned down Mr Martin's marriage proposals.

i. Harriet shouldn't have listened to all of Emma's advice.

j. Mr Elton shouldn't have refused to dance with Harriet.

k. Mr Knightley should have told Emma that he loved her.

l. Mr Churchill shouldn't have let his wife control Frank's life.

Page 139 – exercise 4

a. for you and Frank to be married.

b. most lovely and talented young women in England as your future daughter-in-law.

c. that Mr Knightley must marry no one but herself.

d. first with Mr Knightley, first in interest and affection.

e. I might be able to speak about it more.

f. as no other woman in England would have borne it.

g. am the child of good fortune

h. fall in love with more than three men in one year!

Page 140 – exercise 5

Open answers.

The Upper Classes

Page 143 – exercise 1

a. F – He has more liberal ideas than Emma, but he does nothing to change the class distinctions.

b. F – There was a clear difference between the two.

c. T

d. F – People like Miss Bates were treated with kindness and support.

Page 143 – exercise 2

Open answers.

1 **Secret Loves**

Possible answers:

a. – Jane goes to get her post by herself.
– Frank returns to London as soon as he arrives in Highbury (to order the piano).
– Jane accepts the job as governess because she has just argued with Frank.
– At the ball, Frank rushes out to protect Jane with his umbrella.

b. – Emma becomes upset when Mrs Weston suggests that Mr Knightley

might be in love with Jane.
– At the ball Emma feels sad because Mr Knightley is not dancing.
– It is always clear that she is not really in love with Frank Churchill when she imagines him proposing she always turns him down.

c. – The primary clue is that Mr Knightley is clearly jealous of Frank Churchill when he believes that Emma is in love with him.
– Also, we know that he is a straightforward, honest man, and so when he constantly criticises Emma we can guess that he does it because he loves her and wants her to be a better person.

d. – The mystery of the love between Frank and Jane is a mystery for everybody except the two lovers themselves.
– Emma and Mr Knightley's love is a mystery to everybody, including the two lovers.

2 Defects

Emma: her imagination is greater than her understanding. In other words, once she has imagined something she seems to ignore all evidence to the contrary. This applies, above all, to herself since she does not realise that she is actually in love with Mr Knightley.

Frank Churchill: he is not serious and honest with his friends, and he is willing to play with their feelings.

Mrs Elton: she is pompous and arrogant. She is also cruel for no real reason, as when she tried to hurt Harriet to punish Emma.

Harriet: she does not show much character as can be seen from her slavish following of everything Emma tells her.

Jane Fairfax: her main defect is that she is too reserved, even with those who might be her friends.

Mr Woodhouse: he complains too much, and lets his worries rule his life.

3 Love and Marriage

a. Money was essential but it was not everything.

b. Social position was essential. In short, those of the upper class, wanted to marry someone of the same class with money.

c. Love was important but it was just one of the ingredients needed to make a successful marriage. The others were money and social position. Marrying for love alone would have seemed absurd to them.

d. Jane Austen puts particular emphasis on the moral character of people. Mr Knightley is the 'hero' of the novel because he is always honest and straightforward, even at the cost of offending the woman he loves.
Emma, on the other hand, has to grow morally. The novel, in fact, tells of her growth in moral and spiritual terms. She not only learns to know herself, but she also learns to act better with those around her. Her insulting of Miss Bates is exemplary.

4 Marrying for Survival

a. Harriet and Jane are both orphans, and we see, with Jane in particular, that if she does not get married she will be condemned to the lonely life of a governess.

b. Emma's situation is easier because she is the mistress of Hartfield, and thus will have an easier time attracting a husband, and, perhaps more importantly, she will not be condemned to a life of poverty if she does not marry. This may be the reason why she is so frivolous at the start of the book.

5 **A Good Marriage and a Bad Marriage**

a. The Eltons:
– met at a resort, and so it is implied that their love is a superficial sort of thing;
– are rather vindictive and cruel people;
– Mrs Elton is too concerned with outward appearance: her adoration of the barouche-landau reveals this particular defect.

Emma and Mr Knightley:
– although somewhat superficial at the beginning, Emma shows us her growth and arrival at self-awareness and, by the end of the book, she is on the same moral level as Mr Knightley;
– Mr Knightley seems to be a perfect gentleman: he is honest, kind and loyal. Also, of course, he comes from a good family and has money.

b. Despite the differences in moral character, both couples respect the need to marry people within their own social class with money. Mr Knightley, quite reasonably – and the Eltons would have agreed with him – thinks that Mr Martin is the perfect match for Harriet, a penniless orphan. Mr Elton is shocked when he learns that Emma thought he was in love with Harriet, a penniless orphan.

6

1. D   **2.** B   **3.** B   **4.** C   **5.** D   **6.** A
7. D   **8.** B   **9.** A   **10.** A   **11.** A   **12.** C
13. C   **14.** D   **15.** C   **16.** A   **17.** B

BLACK CAT ENGLISH CLUB
Membership Application Form

BLACK CAT ENGLISH CLUB is for those who love English reading and seek for better English to share and learn with fun together.

Benefits offered:
- *Membership Card*
- *Book discount coupon*
- *English learning e-forum*
- *English learning activities*
- *Black Cat English Reward Scheme*
- *Surprise gift and more...*

Simply fill out the application form below and fax it back to **2565 1113** or send it back to the address at the back.

Join Now! It's FREE exclusively for readers who have purchased *Black Cat English Readers* !

(Please fill out the form with **BLOCK LETTERS**.)

The title of Black Cat English Reader/book set that you have purchased: _____

English Name: _____ (Surname) _____ (Given Name)

Chinese Name: _____

Address:

Tel: _____ Fax: _____

Email: _____
(Login password for e-forum will be sent to this email address.)

Sex: ❏ Male ❏ Female

Education Background: ❏ Primary 1-3 ❏ Primary 4-6 ❏ Junior Secondary Education (F1-3) ❏ Senior Secondary Education (F4-5) ❏ Matriculation ❏ College ❏ University or above

Age: ❏ 6 - 9 ❏ 10 - 12 ❏ 13 - 15 ❏ 16 - 18 ❏ 19 - 24 ❏ 25 - 34 ❏ 35 - 44 ❏ 45 - 54 ❏ 55 or above

Occupation: ❏ Student ❏ Teacher ❏ White Collar ❏ Blue Collar ❏ Professional ❏ Manager ❏ Business Owner ❏ Housewife ❏ Others (please specify: _____)

As a member, what would you like **BLACK CAT ENGLISH CLUB** to offer:
❏ Member gathering/ party ❏ English class with native teacher ❏ English competition
❏ Newsletter ❏ Online sharing ❏ Book fair
❏ Book discount ❏ Others (please specify: _____)

Other suggestions to **BLACK CAT ENGLISH CLUB**: _____

Please sign here: _____ (Date: _____)

Visit us at Quality English Learning Online http://publish.commercialpress.com.hk/qel